Barry Humphries' perennial success and his popularity with an increasingly heterogeneous international public have delighted all but a handful of curmudgeonly Australian journalists who are destined, alas, ever to remain strangers to Fame. His comic theatrical inventions have become accepted as national archetypes and Dame Edna Everage is the preferred role model for most of Australia's female achievers, albeit that the ventripotent, Fescennine and priapic Ambassador, Sir Les Patterson, not seldom elicits from his countrymen an incredulous howl like that of Caliban on beholding his own reflection.

Mr Humphries is an accomplished landscape painter, bibliophile and sometime music-hall artiste. His books, translated into most European languages, are hugely popular, his stage shows enthusiastically patronized and his charming society much sought after by hostesses. Withal, he remains a pleasant and approachable person and a patriotic Australian.

BARRY HUMPHRIES

THE LIFE AND DEATH
OF SANDY STONE

PENGUIN BOOKS

PENGUIN BOOKS

Published by the Penguin Group
Penguin Books Ltd, 27 Wrights Lane, London W8 5TZ, England
Penguin Books USA Inc., 375 Hudson Street, New York, New York 10014, USA
Penguin Books Australia Ltd, Ringwood, Victoria, Australia
Penguin Books Canada Ltd, 10 Alcorn Avenue, Toronto, Ontario, Canada M4V 3B2
Penguin Books (NZ) Ltd, 182–190 Wairau Road, Auckland 10, New Zealand

Penguin Books Ltd, Registered Offices: Harmondsworth, Middlesex, England

First published by Pan Macmillan Publishers Australia,
a division of Pan Books (Australia) Pty Ltd, 1990
This wholly revised edition published by Penguin Books 1991
1 3 5 7 9 10 8 6 4 2

Printed in England by Clays Ltd, St Ives plc

To

Tessa, Emily, Oscar and **Rupert,**

with love:

this street directory to my youth

and

to the cherished memory of

John Betjeman

who always had a lot of time

for

Sandy and Beryl

CONTENTS

ACKNOWLEDGEMENTS

IN EXCAVATING the rich archeological sites of Glen Iris, Hartwell, Mont Albert, Deepdene, Ivanhoe and the Old City of Melbourne, the author gratefully acknowledges the valuable suggestions of his friends Edward Clarke, Neil Munro and Ian Davidson.

Illustrations have been drawn from a number of sources. The sketch of Sandy Stone by the author and the Sidney Nolan drawing of Sandy are both in the possession of the author, and were first reproduced in *A Nice Night's Entertainment* (Currency Press, Australia, 1981). The vignette of 36 Gallipoli Crescent, Glen Iris, is by Andrew Baird and was first published in *Shades of Sandy Stone* (the Tragara Press, Edinburgh, 1989). The print was supplied by the Museum of Performing Arts, Melbourne, and by John Timbers.

The advertisements were reproduced in *The Australian Poster Album*, Brian Carroll (Macmillan 1974); *The Australian Advertising Album*, Brian Carroll (Macmillan 1975); *The Baby Boomers*, Helen Townsend (Simon and Schuster 1988); and *The Weekly*, Denis O'Brien (Penguin 1982). Illustrations also came from the Nestlé Group, Morphy Richards, Sabco Limited, Namco Cookware, Fowler's Vacola, the Coles Myer Archive, *Ads That Made Australia* (Doubleday Australia 1981), the *Herald and Weekly Times*; grateful thanks to the 3LO listeners who kindly lent material for use in this book and to Katharine Brisbane of Currency Press who first published some of this material.

The Clive James 'appreciation' (page xiii) comes from 'Approximately in the vicinity of Barry Humphries', in *Snake Charmers in Texas* by Clive James (Jonathan Cape, London 1988).

My thanks also to Caz Hildebrand for all her work on this Penguin edition.

36 Gallipoli Crescent, Glen Iris

APPRECIATIONS

... HE [Humphries] is also a satirist of Australiana who cuts too close to the awful truth to be considered simply funny. He has the modern Australian way-of-life stretched out and pinned down with needles. He has us taped in killing caricature: our accent, intonation, vocabulary ('had a bit of strife parking the vehicle'), the shattered syntax, the activities, accessories, diet – and through it all the ghastly proprieties, the crazily clumsy genteelness of brick-area suburbia.

Robin Boyd, 1958.

Sandy Stone is one side of Barry Humphries' genius. He is a fig-ure whose prototype can be found in most parts of the Western

World, the decent, honest, kind-hearted, but deeply conventional man who takes life as it comes.

John Betjeman, 1961.

In one of his records an elderly Aussie recalls to himself – like some old bull chewing the cud of memory – the advertisement slogans that have long fascinated his brain and heart. The extraordinary feat here is that this soliloquy, which would be unbearably boring in reality, takes on, in Humphries' gifted interpretation, the qualities both of a penetrating character study of the old man and a sort of demonstration of the dual element of the ordinary and the wonderful in Australian life.

Colin MacInnes, 1965.

An old man – the voice is sexless and ageless with disappointment – speaks a litany of names of nearly half an hour. Patent medicines, breakfast foods, old film stars, snatches of popular songs, Melbourne suburban stations, follow one upon another by every conceivable associative process. The final effect of this poem is anthropological: it is as if the listener had been present at the construction and decay of a mythical society.

Julian Jebb, 1969.

The accepted wisdom is that Sandy Stone is Humphries' most rounded character. If he is, it is partly because of the physical immobility: Humphries is a hypermanically physical actor who with his other characters gets a lot of effects from stage business, so with catatonic Sandy he is obliged to put more into the writing. But the main reason for Sandy's satisfying density of texture is that Humphries is not taking revenge on him. Humphries, for once feeling more complicity than contempt, is at his most poetic with Sandy because he is at his least satirical. To Sandy, and to Sandy alone, he is fair.

Clive James, 1988.

Sandy is the creation of a man of genius. For Barry Humphries is like Henry Lawson and Patrick White. In his character of Sandy Stone he has asked us to look into the mirror and see ourselves as we were and are.

Sandy could drape a mantle of gentle tragedy over the world of suburbia. Sandy knew the one big thing: we all want to be remembered. Sandy knew about death. The death of a human being was like a garden flower that had not been watered – it was a 'goner'. Sandy was like the preacher in the Book of Ecclesiastes: he knew it was all vanity, all empty and a vexation of spirit. He knew there was no essential difference between human beings and the beasts of the field, that they all died and were seen no more. But Sandy had a warm and loving heart. He had the will to endure the end with dignity and courage.

Professor Manning Clark

When Mr Humphries first appeared in London some critics complained, as such people do when confronted with the unfamiliar, that there were a lot of parochial in-jokes and going down down-under memory lane, that they were baffling and inaccessible to the blessedly uninitiated. This struck me as odd, if predictable, because for me he long ago, by the simple power of his poetic instinct and genius, created something that was not there before. That is to say, Australia. Humphries' Australia. It may not be real but one doesn't demand that it should be. It is as real as Cobbett's England, Trollope's Barchester or Swift's Lilliput. Mr Humphries, by isolating its horrors to his own land and private experience, his charity, as well as his mockery and desolation in this most desolate of present landscapes, has turned it into poetry instead of journalism or sociology; a rare enough thing to do in itself.

John Osborne

THE BIRTH OF SANDY STONE

IN 1956, AS A student actor, I came to live in Sydney. Then as now, it seemed raffish and alien to a person from leafy, rectilinear Melbourne. After a few days in a King's Cross lodging house called The Rembrandt, where I encountered my first cockroach, I moved to Lang Road, Centennial Park, on the Bondi tram route. This was a street skirting the swampy, forlorn and by Melbourne standards sparsely arborated parkland, named in commemoration of Sydney's 1888 centenary. Its houses all faced across the road towards the elephantine Moreton Bay figs and coral trees of the park, and were formerly the unlovely mansions of bookmakers, abortionists and speculative builders. Their style was indeterminate; an inflated yet debased variant of Arts and Crafts, where rusticated stone, stucco, 'tapestry brick', shingle and bottle green half-timbering gauchely united. I suppose they represented the 'Federation Style' long before Real Estate agents invented the epithet. When I arrived in Lang Road with my suitcase, the neighbourhood had declined and these rambling villas were mostly sub-divided into bed-sitting rooms. (In recent years they have been restored to private residences by people from Advertising and the Gown and Mantle business.)

In spite of the fact that I was working hard as a revue artiste at the Philip Street Theatre – Australia's most insouciant company – the journey 'home' on the tram, past the fumid and raucous taverns of Oxford Street towards the Centennial Park's gloomy portal, was dispiriting. Awaiting me was the small room with its treacly wainscot and curio ledge, a sagging pink chenille bed, and in the morning, breakfast in the large shared kitchen where I caught glimpses of my fellow tenants; mostly aged and itinerant, and all lonely.

I remember writing a few short stories at this period; imaginative and perhaps even patronizing reconstructions of the lives of the other solitary breakfasters. I had all these stories professionally typed and I submitted them to one or two 'advanced' journals. I neither kept a copy nor received by return of post any of my presumably rejected manuscripts. Only one survived (*vide* 'Sandy Stone's Big Week', Appendix B).

Compared with my life in exile in Sydney, Melbourne, for all the oppressive dreariness of its suburbia, began to acquire a nostalgic effulgence. I even looked back with a sentimental attachment to those mornings only a couple of years before, when I had set off every day from my parents' house to catch the 8 o'clock train to my first and only real job. Then I was employed by a wholesaler of gramophone records, and as the train clattered into Melbourne every morning, I would stand in my first class non-smoker, decorated with sepia pre-war photographic views of Victorian beauty spots, consumed with pity and contempt for my fellow commuters. It occurs to me as I write these words that some of them may still be making the same journey every morning at eight, unfolding their copies of the *Age* or the *Sun News-Pictorial* at precisely the same moment, as the train jolts out of Willisonstation on its journey to the byzantine terminus at Flinders Street.

Some of these commuters I would meet on the road to the station as I ran (always late) to catch my train. Mr Whittle was one; a childless neighbour of my parents to whom I would often chat. He was always on time, always pleasant, and on beholding me, no more than a schoolboy, he would invariably give the crown of his grey trilby a polite and old-fashioned little squeeze. Mr Whittle came to epitomize not merely my parents' generation, but Respectability itself. He represented punctuality, industry, courtesy, thrift, temperance, niceness.

And yet, languishing in my alien Sydney bed-sit, I missed those tedious and perfunctory dialogues with Mr Whittle on the road to the station; his light, dry voice with its slight crackle like a dead gum leaf, and the returned serviceman's badge which glinted dimly on his lapel and suggested that he had once, long ago, participated in some exciting adventure to which the rest of his life constituted a prolonged anti-climax.

At Centennial Park I had written a short story about him (*vide* Appendix B) or someone like him, in my new style: no longer purple and ninety-ish, but drier and more etiolated like its subject, and influenced by Gertrude Stein's portraits and some tales by Paul Bowles which I had picked up in Dymock's second-hand department. I had thought of calling my nice man of the suburbs 'Dusty' after the personage in Eliot's 'Sweeney Agonistes'. I felt that I was exploring the last and most inaccessible region of Australia, as yet undescribed and undiscovered: the Suburbs where most Australians lived. To express the rage, frustration and tedium which they imposed on me in my youth, I needed to invent a technique which was monumentally, grindingly prosaic.

At school and, later, university, together with a group of enthusiastic Dadaists, I had helped reconstitute suburban conversations overheard on trams, crossed telephone lines, over fences and in the street. John Perry(1933–), a brilliant and ferociously anarchic artist and poet, had displayed in those far off years an extraordinary talent for assembling from the scraps and shards of overheard conversations whole speeches and tirades which elevated Australian colloquial discourse to an epic level. At least one of his recorded diatribes anticipates Lucky's speech from *Waiting for Godot* by a good three years. Together we improvized conversations like this:

'Hello, Jim.'

'Hello, Jim.'

'I haven't seen you in donkey's years. how's the world treating you?'

'I haven't seen you in donkey's years either. How's the world treating you?'

'Can't complain.'

'Can't grumble.'

'How's the wife?'

'Lorraine? She's getting on like a BOMB!!' etc.

Slowly the conversation became more irrational and violent, simultaneously more abstract. The characters not only had the same name but they spoke with the same stylized Australian accent, with products and place names deliberately mispronounced or shouted in order to disorient and wrong-foot the audience. When I say audience, it should be noted that our only audience was ourselves, and the private phonograph recordings we made in a booth at Luna Park at this time were entirely for our own amusement. The one theatrical presentation this material ever received was on the campus of Melbourne University one lunchtime in 1953, during a revue entitled *Call Me Madman*. At the conclusion of the performance, an affronted audience of earnest undergraduates, provoked beyond endurance by the relentless and humourless reiteration of such fatuous exchanges, stormed the stage.

I had always felt that the Australian dialect was most imprecisely rendered in stage and radio productions – somehow the accent was either too broad or rendered in a kind of weird

Americanized Cockney. I suppose Australian actors at that time had tried so hard to erase all traces of their origins that when called upon to impersonate an Australian they had had to resort to this bizarre vocal stereotype.

One blustery winter's afternoon in 1956 I was strolling along Bondi Beach, a once attractive bay, long since blighted by hideous apartment buildings, moribund pine trees and raw sewage. In the course of this disconsolate stroll, I inquired the time of a wiry old fellow aged about sixty-five with thin sandy hair and rosy, finely capillaried cheeks, two-tone cardigan and a pair of freckled marsupial paws. This old character addressed me in a voice which I recognized as typical of his age and class: thin, high and dry, seemingly the antithesis of the rugged Australian stereotype. He consulted his watch. 'Approximately in the vicinity of half past five,' he announced with an unmistakable sibilance, no doubt enhanced by ill-fitting teeth. I returned to my bed-sitting room at Centennial Park and, still with gritty memories of Bondi, excised 'Dusty' from my short story and replaced him with Sandy.

It was years before I saw a copy of that work of comic genius, George and Weedon Grossmith's *Diary of a Nobody*, but at this time I was reading Gertrude Stein's *Three Lives* – still one of my favourite books. I also possessed Samuel Beckett's *Watt* in the original Olympia Press edition – then probably the only copy of this remarkable novel in Australia. The droll, pathetic and etiolated personages in these works had their influence on the making of Sandy.

I never thought Alexander Horace Stone ever had much future as a theatrical character. He was, in fact, anti-theatrical; a personage created with the intention of boring an audience into some kind of confrontation with their lives. An arrogant and withal snobbish ambition as I see it now, but the character of Sandy was a satirical conception. Occasionally I would improvise a Sandy monologue as an anti-social party turn, but it never occurred to me to present him on stage. Back in Melbourne two years later, my friend and mentor, Peter O'Shaughnessy, introduced me to an Austrian couple who had begun producing 'microgroove' recordings of poetry and prose. On his recommendation, Peter and Ruth Mann decided to publish a small 'forty-five' of one of my recent monologues, in which I caricatured a genteel Melbourne housewife called Mrs Everage. The 'B' side presented a problem and at O'Shaughnessy's suggestion I wrote and recorded Sandy Stone's 'Days of the Week' with a sleeve note by the architect and critic Robin Boyd. It was released in 1958 and became an enormous cult and subsequently popular success.

Later that year, in a revue on which O'Shaughnessy and I collaborated, he proposed that I bring Sandy to the stage and apostrophize the audience, wearing a fawn dressing gown and clutching a hot water bottle. With very little confidence in the merits of this idea, I grudgingly assented. We had decided that in the interludes in Sandy's monologue bridging the days of the week, the pianist should tinkle something unfashionable and nostalgic like 'Silver Threads Amongst the Gold', 'Little Man You've Had a Busy Day' and 'When You Grow Too Old to Dream'. The effect on a Melbourne audience in the late 1950s was electric and convulsive. Although the monologue was stylized and so uncomfortably close to home, they laughed as though regaled by the best joke they had ever heard. Fortunately, the word catharsis was not in current use, or I might have sententiously claimed to have induced it.

Thereafter, up until the present time, I have been at pains to include a Sandy Stone monologue as the *adagio* or *lento* movement in all my stage shows. Over the last ten years, British audiences have developed a liking for his ruminations. More recently, in fact since his death, Sandy has become more vigorous, broader, even at times jocose; but he still has his roots in the shallow, grey soil of Melbourne's eastern suburbs, and his station-bound ghost with its collapsed Gladstone bag still flits downhill past the frosty gardens on July mornings at seven fifty-one. For although Melbourne may change – in places out of all recognition – one has only to step off the main road, down a secluded suburban side street in East Malvern or Camberwell or Hartwell or Ashburton or Glen Iris, to re-enter the immutable, cosy, exhilaratingly dull labyrinth of Australian life.

Cintra, 1990

WILD LIFE IN SUBURBIA

THE PIECE WHICH FOLLOWS took final shape in 1958 and was specially written for the gramophone record *Wild Life in Suburbia*. I had recently been introduced to Peter Mann of Score Records who had issued some very successful recordings of Australian verse and it was thought that two of my monologues might make an amusing EP. I performed Edna Everage's 'Olympic Hostess' sketch on Side One whilst Side Two accommodated my newly developed old man with the prosaic gravel voice whom I christened 'Sandy Stone', with its mineral overtones and its further echo of the then popular Sydney radio detective 'Randy' Stone. Peter Mann issued the disc from his Glen Iris studio in Melbourne in a handsome sleeve designed by Max Robinson to which the architect Robin Boyd appended a complimentary blurb. The enterprise proved a huge success and this record and the two which followed it achieved a remarkably wide circulation in Australia and beyond.

Later in the same year I performed Sandy Stone's 'Days of the Week' on the stage of the New Theatre in Flinders Street, Melbourne. I had never intended to do the character of Sandy Stone myself for I felt that Sandy's voice sounded more hypnotic droning from a gramophone speaker than from the lips of a tall, skinny, long-haired actor; but at the director's insistence I delivered the monologue, in pyjamas and dressing gown, from a moth-eaten 'Genoa velvet' armchair, dimly spotlit. The piano interrupted Sandy's grindingly banal recollections with sentimental airs of the thirties and forties. I did not know it then, but with this tribute on the altar of Mnemosyne Australian Nostalgia was born. Sandy is still the *adagio* act in all my stage productions.

Sandy's more convivial activities – the occasional shandy, attendance at sporting fixtures and visits to the RSL – occur less frequently in the chronicles which follow. He becomes increasingly abstemious and withdrawn, and although he may once have smoked or rolled his own (*vide* 'Sandy Stone's Big Week', Appendix B) no cigarette has yet been extinguished in the omnipresent smoker's companion.

•Sandy, in pyjamas and dressing gown, is discovered seated in a shabby armchair. He addresses the audience.

I WENT to the RSL[1] the other night and had a very nice night's entertainment. Beryl, that's the wife, came along too. Beryl's not a drinker but she had a shandy. She put in quite a reasonable quantity of time yarning with Norm Purvis's good lady and I had a beer with old Norm and some of the other chappies there. I don't say no to the occasional odd glass and Ian Preston, an old friend of mine, got up and sang a few humorous numbers – not too blue, on account of the womenfolk – so that altogether it was a really nice type of night's entertainment for us both. We called it a day round about ten-ish; didn't want to make it too late a night as Beryl had a big wash on her hands on the Monday morning and I had to be in town pretty early, stocktaking and one thing and another.

Well, we got back to Gallipoli Crescent about twenty past and Beryl and I went to bed.

We were very glad we hadn't made it too late a night on the Sunday because the Chapmans were expecting us over on the Monday night for a

---

1 • The Returned Servicemen's League.

couple of hours to look at some slides of their trip. They're a very nice type of person and some of the coloured pictures he'd taken up north were a real ... picture. Vi Chapman had gone to a lot of trouble with the asparagus rolls and altogether it was a really lovely night's entertainment for the two of us. Educational, too. Well, round about ten I said we'd have to be toddling. You see, we didn't want to make it too late a night because Tuesday was the Tennis Club picture night and Beryl had a couple of tickets.

Well, there's not much I can say about the Tuesday, except that it was a really lovely night's entertainment. We're not ones for the pictures as a rule but when we do go we like to see a good bright show. After all, there's enough unhappiness and sadness in the world without going to see it in the theatre. Had a bit of strife parking the vehicle – you know what it's like up around that intersection near the Civic. Anyway, we found a possie[2] in the long run just when we were beginning to think we might miss the blessed newsreel. The newsreel had a few shots of some of the poorer type of Italian housing conditions on the Continent and it

---

2 • (*pron.* pozzy). Hypocorism for position, in this case a parking spot. Abbreviation of words with the 'ie' infantile ending is popular in Australia, as in 'Chrissie pressie' or 'hyzzie at the hozzie' (hysterectomy at the hospital).

made Beryl and I realize just how fortunate we were to have the comfort of our own home and all the little amenities round the home that make life easier for the womenfolk, and the menfolk generally, in the home. We left soon after the interval as the next show wasn't the best and I was feeling a bit on the tired side. Besides, Beryl was expecting her sister and her husband over for Five Hundred[3] on the Wednesday and we didn't want to make it too late a night.

So, Beryl and I went to bed.

Had to slip out of the office on the Wednesday lunch hour to get a few cashews to put round the card table. Beryl was running up a batch of sponge fingers[4] with the passionfruit icing. There's no doubt about it, Beryl makes a lovely sponge finger.

Well, the card night went off very nicely indeed, except that Beryl's sister Lorna got a bit excited during the Five Hundred and knocked over a cup of tea and a curried egg sandwich on the new carpet. Oh, she was very apologetic, but as I said to Beryl later, saying sorry won't buy you a new

---

3 • A popular family card game.

4 • Known in England as 'boudoir fingers', a confection frequently served stale as an accompaniment to fruit salad or chopped, variegated jelly. These flattened oblongs of sponge, spatulate at their extremities, are sometimes iced.

wall-to-wall. And you know what curried egg does to a burgundy Axminster.

By and large though, all things considered, and taking everything into account, it was a pretty nice night's entertainment.

They left early-ish. And Beryl and I went to bed ...

Thursday was a bit quiet at the office and I was just as glad because I'd been feeling a bit more on the tired side than usual. Beryl had another fitting that night. She's having a new frock made for Geoff and Janice's wedding at Holy Trinity on the twenty-first and she wants to wear something a bit special – you know what the womenfolk are like. Anyway, I dropped her off at the dressmaker's on the way to the Lodge.

It was a bit on the lateish side when I got home and I went straight to bed and we had a very nice night's ... rest.

Always glad when Friday comes. Beryl and I usually have a nice quiet night in the home. It's the only chance I get to view the TV. There's usually a good story on of a Friday night on the Kool Mint Theatre of the Capital Air – or else an educational quiz. Beryl had been down to the Town Hall library and got herself the latest Georgette

Heyer so that, between the two of us, we had a nice night's home entertainment. We'd had a run of late nights and we were both pretty fagged so round about ten I filled the hottie and Beryl and I went to bed.`

I was glad we hadn't made it too late a night as we had to be down the junction pretty early on the Saturday morning for the weekend shopping. Had a bit of strife parking the vehicle though. You know what it's like at the junction of a Saturday morning. However, I found a nice possie in the long run, just when were beginning to think we might miss the blessed butcher. I had a few minutes' worry though. I lost Beryl in the Foodorama but she had the good sense to go back to the car.

I got home in time for a bit of lunch and then I had to whiz out again to the football. Beryl stayed at home to do the week-end baking.

Had the usual trouble parking the vehicle. You know what it's like at Memorial Park on a Saturday arvo. However, found a possie in the long run, just when I was thinking I'd be late for the bounce. Oh, you wouldn't catch me missing an important semi. Beryl had packed me a nice Thermos of Milo[5] and I was pretty glad of it. It's very cold and blowy in the outer.

Had a bit of trouble shifting the vehicle. You know what it's like at Memorial Park after a big match – utility wedged right there in front of me. However, I got out in the long run, just when I was beginning to think Beryl would have to wait tea. By the time I got home it was *that* blowy, the *Herald* [6] was all over the front lawn.

Next door had invited us in to hear their *My Fair Lady* record but I'd already heard it about seventeen or eighteen times. In point of fact, it was their particular microgroove I had heard in view of the fact that their new Stromberg-Carlson radio-gram is a bit on the loudish side. Anyway, we'd had a very nice afternoon's entertainment and Beryl wasn't that keen, so we made an early night of it and went to bed.

I always clean the car of a Sunday morning and do a bit of pottering in the garden. Bit worried about those rhodies.

---

5 • A sedative chocolate drink.

6 • Melbourne's evening newspaper, now sadly amalgamated, of strikingly uneven quality. Newspapers were home delivered in Australia by being flung over the nature strip and front fence with uncertain accuracy from a bicycle or van. If not retrieved they were invariably riffled and dispersed by the ceaseless wind.

Had the roast midday as we only like a light tea if we're going out of a Sunday night: nice bit of corned beef with a drop of Beryl's homemade chutney, some nice mashed potatoes, some nice lettuce stained with beetroot, a few nice scones and apricot jam and a nice cup of tea. Saves a big wash-up.

I'm really looking forward to the RSL tonight because – if you can go by experience – it ought to be a very nice night's entertainment.

Serve It Ice Cold
Nature's own appetiser and a grand drink, Rosella Tomato Juice with the *true fresh Tomato Flavour.*

Rosella

VITAMIN RICH

TOMATO JUICE

2

DEAR BERYL

THIS EPISTOLARY MONOLOGUE has never been performed on stage. It was written for Peter Mann's Score label early in 1959, just before I sailed off to Venice on the *Toscana*. (Mrs Everage sang her lilting 'Highett Waltz' dedicated to a new Melbourne suburb on the other side of the record.)

Many years before, I had devised a character called Graham Polkinghorn whose ghostly presence emerged from a series of rambling letters intoned by his mother (*vide* Appendix A). In the mid-fifties I could rarely be dissuaded from reciting these lugubrious and uneventful missives at parties, which they invariably brought to a close. At the end of the sketch Graham's tabid mother dies in Melbourne so that the final letter to reach Graham in London is from a neighbour who lists a large number of other neighbours who were at the funeral and all 'wished to be

remembered'. I adapted the same idea in this Sandy Stone monologue and was to do so again, following the 'Dear Graham' letters
more closely, in 'The Land of the Living' (1971).

Although I identified Sandy's suburb as Glen Iris in this
monologue, I had obviously forgotten this when I wrote 'Sandy
Agonistes' which follows this script. There I trace his journey
home to the suburb of Mont Albert. Moreover, when the character first appeared in a short story in 1958 (*vide* Appendix B) his
address was Humoureske Street (Edna's street?), Hartwell. In the
early years of this creation, admittedly, I had not sought to precisely locate him anywhere but in a suburban limbo.

Kia Ora,

36 Gallipoli Crescent,

Glen Iris.[1]

DEAR BERYL,

By the time this letter reaches you you'll be in the
Old Country. I was thrilled to get your post card
from Aden and sorry the smell was so bad, darling. I'm glad you found your sea legs.

Everyone is asking after you. Yesterday I had a
tinkle from Nora Manly to see if I'd heard from
you yet. I gave her your last news and she asks to

1• A select Melbourne suburb.

be remembered. It's not worth stopping *Woman's Day,* is it? I told her she could pop round every week and borrow it till you get back. She also wondered if she could borrow the loan of your Georgette Heyers. She's a pretty careful type of person, isn't she, so I said yes. She mentioned it was a pity we couldn't have both gone abroad together so I told her it's not what you want to do in this life but what you can afford to do. Money doesn't grow on trees. Besides I've got plenty to do on the home front to keep me out of mischief – got my hands pretty full at work at the moment and the garden gets very thirsty this time of the year.

You remember we had a card from the MacLeods? Well you remember old Mrs MacLeod Senior – we met her down at Mordialloc[2] that Xmas – well, you'll be sorry to hear she fell asleep last Tuesday. She was well on into the

The Traveller's Companion!

Dr. Morse's
INDIAN
ROOT
PILLS

When packing up for a trip be sure and place a bottle of Dr. Morse's Indian Root Pills in a handy position in your suit-case.

The changes of food and living conditions upset the Liver and other digestive organs, causing Biliousness, Constipation, and Indigestion, thus rendering necessary the use of Dr. Morse's Indian Root Pills to restore the system to proper working order.

Dr. Morse's
INDIAN ROOT PILLS
– for the Liver

---

2 • A charming Melbourne bayside resort.

eighties so I suppose you'd say she'd had her life.

Also, I'm afraid, my darling, the big hyder-ange's a goner. That side of the house was always a bad spot and last Thursday was an absolute scorcher. When I got home the place was like an oven, although I always close the venetians before I take off in the morning.

I was out giving the silver birch a drink the other night and who should come across the street for a bit of a yarn but Mr Rust. Well, I've never had much time for him myself and you always said you thought she was a bit ordinary. They've never been what you'd call neighbourly, have they? Always kept themselves to themselves – see them in the street and they wouldn't say boo. Anyway the funny part about it, he seemed quite a reasonable type of chappie – a real family man. His two kiddies have gone back to school as brown as berries. Apparently they've got a very nice beach place down Rosebud[3] way. Funny part about it – to look at him you wouldn't think he had a blessed razoo.

I've had a few of my meals over at the Long-mires lately. She'd said anytime, and they've really been very hospitable and made me feel very much

---

3 • A popular Melbourne bayside resort.

at home. I always like a yarn with old Jim. He's still only just so-so, you know – same old tummy trouble. I don't think he ever got over young Horrie going to the pack the way he did – what with getting caught up with the wrong element and a mixed marriage to top it all off. Mind you, we could see it coming, couldn't we, when the little devil wouldn't go into his father's business. It's a terrible thing when parents work and slave all their lives to give their kiddies just a few of the opportunities they never had themselves and they just turn round and bite the hand that feeds them. It nearly killed old Jim – he's spent a small fortune on that boy's education. Grammar[4] and one thing and another.

Well, Beryl, that's just about all the news at present. Business is much of a muchness. I'm enclosing tonight's 'Wally and the Major'.[5] Isn't the waitress the image of Jean? I laughed! He's clever that fellow.

Look after yourself now and send me the odd snap.

Your ever loving

Sandy

---

4 • The Melbourne Grammar School, an expensive boys school.

5• A long-running, syndicated daily newspaper cartoon set in the canefields of Queensland, by Australia's greatest black and white artist, Stan Cross.

P.S. Vi and Alan Chapman, Mr and Mrs Blackett, Bill Lesley, Valda Clissold, Tom and Cheryl Kerr, the Matthews, the Simpsons and old Miss Warner would all like to be remembered.

3

SANDY AGONISTES

IN 1959 I WAS LIVING in London in a Notting Hill Gate basement. From time to time I received a very welcome royalty cheque from Melbourne – proceeds from the still successful *Wild Life in Suburbia* records. I noticed that they were also available in London at John Mitchell's Discurio record shop in Sheperds Market where, unknown to me, they were being snapped up by the poet John Betjeman and distributed to bemused friends like John Osborne, Osbert Lancaster, Cecil Beaton, Alan Moorehead and Elizabeth Cavendish. As a result of Betjeman's perfervid advocacy, some of these recipients actually became lifelong Sandy Stone *aficionados*.

One morning I had an aerogramme from my record producer in Melbourne proposing a new 12-inch record and offering a tempting advance. All I had to do was write and record the new material. I decided against an Edna Everage monologue, since I felt I had exhausted the comic possibilities of this character, and instead devised a monologue for an Australian 'lass' living in an Earl's Court bed-sitting room, complaining about the English and missing Melbourne. London was not lacking in prototypes for this character. I wrote a diatribe for a man called Colin Cartwright, a self-made businessman, fulminating against his children's ingratitude. The third piece was a soliloquy by 'Buster' Thompson, a loutish Melbourne public schoolboy on the tear in Kangaroo Valley.

The question remained as to how I would fill the other side of a 12-inch microgroove record. I decided to go out on a limb and see how much that small coterie of Sandy Stone admirers could stand. I borrowed a tape recorder which had an unusual device – perhaps even a design fault – which made it possible to superimpose one's voice several times over a layer of pre-recorded sound, producing an evocative, three-dimensional echo effect like a sonic cat's cradle. Making much use of this gadget, and guided by a sheaf of notes, I improvized into the machine a litany of city streets, railway stations, brand names and obsolescent advertising slogans, interspersed with snatches of popular song. In Sandy's scratchy falsetto I tried to portray a synthetic and abstracted picture of my parents' Melbourne before the Age of Laminex.[1] Sidney Nolan listened to the tape and was sufficiently awe-struck to draw an image for the sleeve which showed the face of a

1 • Formica.

mustachio'd Sandy emerging from a vase of flowers. Ray Lawler kindly wrote some generous sleeve notes.

'Sandy Agonistes' was not a huge success, but now it is, I understand, a collector's item. It was certainly recorded under the most rudimentary, even primitive, conditions, and one does not have to listen too carefully to the recording to hear the rumble of the big red double-deckers outside my Notting Hill basement window.

Weeties ... Crispies ... Kornies ... Malties ... Granose ... Weet Bix ... Vita-Brits ... Kelloggs Corn Flakes ... Kelloggs All-Bran ... Kelloggs ... Rice Bubbles ... **snap, crackle, pop ...** Semolina ... John Bull Oats ... Phosphatine ... Heinz Tomato Sauce ... Rosella Tomato Soup ... Kia ora Tomato Sauce ... White Crow Tomato Sauce ... AJC Tomato Sauce ... PK Spearmint ... Wrigley's Juicy Fruit Chewing Gum ... Allen's Irish Moss Gum ... Jubes ... Allens Cure-em Quick ... Allen's Butter Menthols – the menthol clears the head and the butter soothes the throat ... Throaties. ✧ **TIME FOR A CAPSTAN–THEY'RE BLENDED BETTER!** ✧ Three Threes always please ... Minties ... BVDs. ✧ **WE, TOO, SMOKE TURF!** ✧ Craven A's ... Columbine Caramels ... Hoadley's Violet

Crumble Bars ... Ford Pills ... Fan-Tales ...
Jaffas ... Sun Buds ... Sun News Pictorial ...
Monty Blandford ... Mont Albert. East Camberwell. Camberwell. Auburn.
Hawthorn. Glenferrie. Burnley. Richmond. East Richmond. **Flinders
Street Station.** Swanston Street. Flinders Lane.
Collins Street. Little Collins Street. Bourke Street. Little Bourke Street.
Lonsdale Street. Little Lon ... Latrobe Street. Spring Street. Exhibition
Street. Russell Street. Swanston Street. Elizabeth Street. Queen Street.
William ... King ... Spencer Street. THE MAN IN GREY . . . **Darrod's
the style store in the heart of Bourke Street. The Myer Emporium
for value and friendly service.** Payne's Bon Marche. Ball and
Welsh's. The Leviathan. Manton's. Acland's. Hick's A. 3DB and 3LK
the Herald stations. **3KZ the brighter broadcasting sta-
tion.** 3AW Melbourne. 3XY. ✧ **WHY
COUGH? TAKE Y-COUGH!** ✧ The
Smile-Away Club. The Myer Musicale. The Lux
Radio Theatre. The Australian Amateur Hour.
Reflections in a Wine Glass. Dick Cranbourne.
Norman Banks. Eric Welsh. Charlie Vaud. The
P&A Parade. Mike Connors. HELLO THE
HOSPITALS! Fred and Maggie Everybody. Dad
and Dave. A George Edwards production. Donald
Day. Daybreak Dan ... David and Dawn ... First
Light Fraser ... One Man's Family ... The Majes-
tic. The State. The Plaza. The Regent. The Capi-
tol. The Metro. The Melba ... The Deluxe ... The

Apollo ... The Princess. The Tivoli. The Bijou. Stiffy and Mo ... Adolphe Menjou ... Jean Harlow ... Clark Gable ... Alice Faye ... The Talmadge Sisters ... Madge Elliott and Cyril Richard ... Fred Astaire and Ginger Rogers ... Mary Astor. Joan Crawford. Jim Gerald. George Wallace. Wallace Beery ... Carole Lombard ... Freddie Bartholomew. Myrna Loy ... *Loy's* Lemonade ... *Foy* & Gibson ... *Roy* ... Cazaly? Wally and the ... Major ... Hatfield's daily dozen ... Chicken Small-horn ... Small's Club Chocolates ... The Choco-late Soldier ... ✧ **NO NO NANETTE!** ✧ Naughty Marietta ... Nelson Eddy and Jeanette MacDonald ... The Desert Song. *'Mine alone, you're mine alone ... Mine alone, you're ...'* The Maid of the Moun-tains. White Horse Inn. Gladys Moncrieff ... ✧ **DOCTOR MORSE'S INDIAN ROOT PILLS.** ✧ Phosphatine ... Kolynos ... Melly Colly ... The Colin Ross Case. Gunn's Alley ... Oop! Rudy Vallee ... Moonee Valley ... *'A Tropical moon, a sleepy lagoon ...'* Palm Court. Palmolive Toilet Soap. Rexona. Ipana. Dromana. Lifebuoy. Life-guard Milk. Sunshine Full Cream Powdered Milk. Creamoata. Wotan. Carbine. Phar Lap. Donald Bradman ... Alan Kippax ... S ... Skipping Girl Vinegar ... The Pyjama Girl ... Charmosan Face

Powder, sifted through silk ... Carter's Little Liver Pilll-l-s ... *'Little old lady passing by, there's a tear in her eye ... eye ...'* Aye, it's me, Doctor Mac ... kenzie's Menthoids. ✧ **ASK THE MAN OUTSIDE HOYTS**.✧ Screen News. ✧ **AGE OR ARGUS, WEEKLY TIMES, LEADER, BULLETIN OR PUNCH!** ✧ The Star ... White Star Starch ... *'A star fell from heaven one beautiful night ...'* Make good night a certainty with Laconia Blank ... Blandford ... Kingsford ... Smith's Weekly ... Table Talk ... ✧ **THERE'S A MAPLE'S STORE RIGHT NEAR YOUR DOOR.** ✧ *My Mabel waits for me underneath a bright blue sky, where the dog sits on the tucker box, five miles from Gundagai'* Gunga Din Snake Gully Ferntree Gully Fernington ✧ **YOU FURNISH WELL AT PPL** . . . ✧ Dudley Flats ... The Elwood canal ... Tatts ... Akubra hats ... Black Cats ... Black Magic ... Old Gold Assortment ... Seppelt's Royal Purple Para. FINE WINE, TINTARA! Kinkara Tea. With C & G's you see with ease ... Easy-Meal ... *'K-k-k-katie, beautiful Katie, you're the only g-g-g-girl that I adore; when the m-moon shines over the cowshed I'll be waiting at the k-k-k-kitchen door'* ... London Stores. London Baby Carriages. Buckley & Nunn's. Buckley's Canadiol Mixture. Pix. ✧**ICE! DIXIE ICE!** ✧ Penny Nestles *'Loora loora loora lay, any umbrellas, any umbrellas to mend today?'* ... *'South of the*

—

border, down Mexico way' ... ✧ **DOCTOR MORSE'S INDIAN ROOT PILLS.** ✧ Blue Gillette. Reckitt's Blue. Luna Park ... Half Moon Bay ... The Palais St Kilda ... ✧ **THE GREAT WALTZ.** ✧ The Great ... War. Wardrop My Tailor. *'Popeye the sailor man, I'm Popeye the sailor man I'll eat all my spinach'* ... ship ... *'On the good ship Lollipop, it's a ... a n ... an ... animal crackers in my soup'* ... Rosella Tomato Soup. Rose Marie. Hosie's Hotel. Young & Jackson's. The Federal. The Lang Government. Lord Huntingdale. Joe Lyons. Laurie Nash. Monash ... ✧ **ASHBURTON-ALAMEIN   LINE TRAIN LEAVING FROM NUMBER TWO PLATFORM, STAND CLEAR PLEASE!** ✧ *'Somewhere over the rainbow, bluebirds fly'* ... Flinders Street. East Richmond. Richmond. Burnley. Glenferrie. Hawthorn. Auburn. Camberwell. East Camberwell. Mont Albert. Allen's Irish Moss Gum Jubes. PK. Spearmint. Wrigley's Juicy Fruit Chewing Gum. Clement's Tonic. Kelloggs Corn Flakes ... Kelloggs Rice Bubbles ... Kelloggs All-Bran ... Kelloggs Rice Bubbles ... Kelloggs All-Bran ... Kelloggs Rice Bubbles...................... *'I'm forever blowing bubbles, pretty bubbles in the air, they fly so high, nearly reach the sky'* ... McAlphine's Self-Raising Flour ... Bert Hinkler. Move the sprinkler! ✧ **CEREBOS SALT – SEE HOW IT RUNS!** ✧ Saunders Malt ... ies ... Granose ... Granny Martin's ... Kornies ... Crispies ... Weeties ...

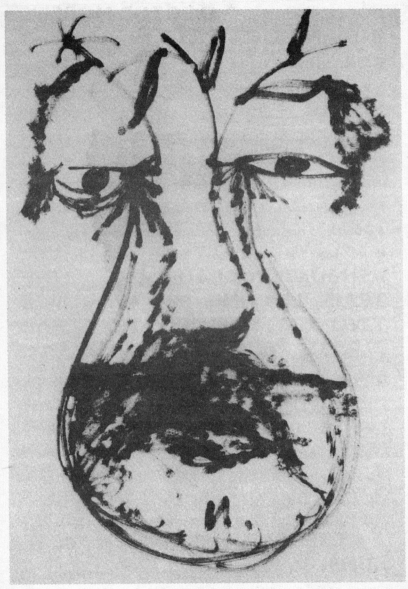

An early impression of Sandy by Sidney Nolan.

4

CAN YOU KEEP A SECRET?

SANDY STONE next shuffled on to the Melbourne stage in 1961 in Clifford Hocking's production of my *A Nice Night's Entertainment* at the Assembly Hall, Collins Street. (It was at Mr Hocking's suggestion that I first contemplated the idea of compiling a one-man show.)

Here I began a long tradition of opening the second half of the show in a low key with a Sandy monologue. The setting was invariably tenebrous: a fawn or brown armchair dimly illuminated by a chrome and Bakelite standard lamp with brown candlewick trim. Dressed in pyjamas and with a fawn chequered dressing gown the colour of dust, Sandy, clutching his clammy hottie, would enter and exit to a piano accompaniment, usually 'When You Grow Too Old to Dream', 'Little Man You've Had a Busy Day' or some other evocative and apposite strain.

• *Before drifting into this monologue, Sandy absently plays an infantile nursery game with his fingers: 'Here's the church and here's the steeple. Open the doors and here's all the people.'*

IT ALL STARTED just prior to last Easter when Phil and Doffie Prentiss sold up their home at 43 Gallipoli Crescent. Between you and me they got a very nice price and Phil told me on the quiet they got what they asked! They sold to an *exceptionally* nice young couple, with a pair of youngsters too who looked as though they'd take a real interest in the garden.

When I first heard the new people were a Clive and Glenda Nettleton it didn't ring a bell but Beryl said to me, Nettleton ... Nettleton ... Nettleton. Then she remembered that Valda Clissold's younger sister Wanda had married a Brian Hiscock, one of *the* Hiscock boys who worked in exactly the same office – so it eventuated – as a Clive Nettleton who had married an old school friend of Wanda's by the name of Glenda Hibbotson and who now had a couple of kiddies – boy six, girl eight. Put it another way. When Beryl was in Bethesda having her veins done she met Valda Clissold, *née* Smoothie, who was in the next bed. They got on like a house on fire and later on, through young Valda, we met her sister Wanda. Now the amazing part about it was that Wanda Hiscock, who was a Wanda Smoothie, had been to school with Glenda Hibbotson, who later on married a Clive Nettleton, who worked in exactly the same office as her husband.

It sounds a bit on the complicated side, I know, but it's not if you think that Valda Clissold who was in Bethesda with Beryl has a brother-in-law, Brian Hiscock – one of *the* Hiscock boys – who worked in exactly the same office as the husband of sister Wanda's old school friend, Glenda Hibbotson.

Isn't it a small world?

Naturally, we made ourselves known and it wasn't very long after that that young Glenda Nettleton was knocking on the back door. A cup of icing sugar; a drop of cochineal; cream of tartar; the odd lemon. I told Beryl to watch it or she'd be letting herself in for a lot of babysitting! And, sure enough, before we knew where we were they were round here for afternoon tea, *plus* young Wayne and Marilyn. Ah, but what a bonzer[1] pair of youngsters they were! A couple of little trimmers.[2]

Clive Nettleton hadn't had a real break from work since the marriage and *she* was a bundle of nerves and as thin as a rake, so seeing as they were tantamount to being friends of ours, through the Smoothie girls, Beryl and I had a bit of a confab in the kitchen and we intimated to them that we were desirous to mind the youngsters for them over the Easter period while they had a bit of a breather down at her people's home.

Well, they hummed and hahed. They said they wouldn't dream of it. They said you don't want a little boy of six and a half and a girl of eight under your feet. I said, don't talk a lot of twaddle. I said the offer's there. You're a young couple – you might as well take the chance while you can! To tell you the truth, we'd fallen for those kiddies like a ton of bricks.

Well, I wouldn't take no for an answer. And

1 • Excellent.

2 • Perfect of their kind.

Glenda Nettleton could see with half an eye that Beryl was *scrupulous* and that the tinies would be well catered for at Kia Ora ...

On the Thursday before Easter I got home from the office early to see if there was anything I could do to help Beryl. I brought home lollies and jelly beans and liquorice allsorts too, but Beryl put her foot down and said I'd spoil their tea. She had everything beautifully under control and she sent me down the street to get some extra milk if the little man was open. I chased all over the blessed shop and by the time I got back Wayne and Marilyn had had their tea and had almost finished their bath. I put my head around the corner to see if I could take over – you know, give the wife a bit of a break – and she sent me into the lounge room to warm their jim-jams.

While I was in there, I had a bit of a hunt through my books for something suitable. *The Herald Pictorial Atlas, The First Year of War in Pictures, The Second Year of War in Pictures, The Third Year of War in Pictures, The Fifth Year of War in Pictures, The Fourth Year of War in Pictures, The Illustrated Family Doctor, Soldiering On, The Great Book of Humour, The Story of the World in*

Pictures. I found a couple of my old Sunday School prizes in the long run, but when Beryl came in to collect their pyjamas she said they'd brought their Noddy books with them. As I was going through one of my cupboards I came across a whole album of my old Hawaiian records, though goodness knows what's happened to the little HMV instrument we used to play them on! 'Hula Moon', 'My Honolulu Baby', 'Ukelele Lady', 'Lovely Hula Hands' – melodies Beryl and I used to dance to *years* ago. Amazing, really, the amount of junk you keep.

Well, the sandman came in the long run. We left the light on in the hall and Beryl and I settled down to watch the instrument ...

On the Good Friday I thought I'd take them up to Wattle Park for a play on the swings and the see-saws and a picnic lunch. I didn't take the vehicle, on account of the Easter toll. We couldn't make a start until lateish, though, as public transport on a Good Friday is very ragtime.[3] Had to phone up the depot and they put me through to a lass who certainly sounded as though she wasn't born on this side of the world.

---

3 • (obs.) Erratic, disorderly.

Beryl had cut some delicious sandwiches. Egg and lettuce. Peanut butter. Vegemite[4] and walnut, cheese and apricot jam. And lots of bread and butter and hundreds and thousands[5] –

and one of her own specialities – a chocolate and banana log. She'd only baked it that morning and the kiddies were most intrigued. Beryl said if they promised to be-have themselves at Wattle Park they could lick the beaters.[6] We packed some of Beryl's home-made ginger beer and a Thermos for ourselves but unfortunately Beryl forgot to put the greaseproof

paper[7] round the cork appertaining to the

4 • A celebrated yeast-based condiment'.

5 • Fairy bread, an essential for tinies' birthday parties.

6• A glossal activity indulged in by privileged Australian children in the early stage of the cake-making process.

7• (obs.) Sometimes called lunchwrap. Translucent paper used before the age of plastics to envelop buttered scones, sandwiches and tennis cake.

calamine lotion bottle we used for the milk with the resultant consequence that by the time we got off the bus the milk had soaked right through the sandwiches and halfway up the log. As if that wasn't enough, it ruined the lining of a lovely raffia bag that Beryl had bought at the Opportunity shop.[8] However, it wasn't altogether wasted as Beryl said she could use it for the pegs.

Not to be deterred, young Wayne and Marilyn were as happy as a couple of sandboys playing round on the swings and seesaws and climbing all over the memorial cannon.[9] However, I didn't want to make it *too* long a day. I was quite anxious to get home and tune into the 3DB[10] Good Friday Appeal. Beryl and I always give a little something but we've never heard ourselves called out. Well, I tried to listen for a while but it was well-nigh impossible. Beryl had buttered some hot cross buns and the kiddies were in their nighties and *crying out* for the instrument ...

---

8 • An emporium of bygones and left-off effects sold for the benefit of charity. (*Vide* 'South of the Border' *passim*.)

9 • Public parks in Australia are liberally dotted with WW1 artillery, 'burnished by generations of infant groins'.

10 • An influential Melbourne wireless station.

On the Saturday morning Wayne and Marilyn were as good as gold, playing out there on the back lawn while Beryl kept an eye on them through the kitchen window. I was round the front, doing a spot of watering. After that summer we had, the nature strip[11] was on its last legs. No rest for the wicked. I jolly nearly forgot their Easter eggs but I shot down the street and caught the little man, who told me that if I'd left it another five minutes I would have been stiff. The eggs I got weren't exactly identical but they were the only two procurable.

We had a good old laugh that afternoon too, I can tell you. Beryl had gone through the camphor chest[12] and dug out a lot of old clothes she'd been meaning to give to the Holy Trinity jumble sale and those kiddies gave us a real concert. Young Marilyn's been having ballet lessons at Madame Thelma's Dance Academy at the Cub Hall on Wednesdays and Fridays and she got up there on her toes and danced like a little fairy. Beryl said that to see that kiddie made her wish she'd kept up with her own lessons. Not to be deterred,

11 • An attractively attended grass verge (American?)separating the frontage of Melbourne (and to some extent Sydney) residences from the roadway and gutter.

12 • Elaborately carved aromatic receptacle for woollies, furs and bridal souvenirs often procured in the orient en route to the Old Country.

young Wayne was all dressed up like Lord Muck – clopping around in a pair of Beryl's high-heeled shoes, lipstick all over his chops, bangles and earrings and goodness knows what. He was wearing everything but the kitchen sink and showing off something terrific too, but we had to laugh! You should have seen his face. It was a picture no artist could paint.

You can't leave them alone five minutes though. They must have got into the camphor chest and dug out an old lingerie box where Beryl keeps some of her very personal things. Anyway, when we came back into the room, they'd eaten icing off a bit of our wedding cake that Beryl had treasured for thirty-two years. What can you say to other people's kiddies? If they'd been children of mine it would have been a case of paddy-whack the drumsticks, and no bones about it.

However, we packed them off and Beryl said if they didn't behave themselves there'd be tears before bedtime and the Easter Bunny wouldn't be calling. It worked like a charm and there wasn't another peep out of them after that. There's no doubt about it – Beryl's marvellous with kiddies.

Well, the Easter bunny did in point of fact call next morning, but there was merry hell to pay. Their eggs weren't exactly identical. Different coloured silver paper; one of them didn't like dark chocolate. Anyway, before we knew where we were, they were fighting like cat and dog. Young Marilyn turned on the waterworks and Wayne, who's a *real little tease*, kept on pulling faces, even though we told him the wind might change. You can't reason with some children. However, they were as right as rain before you could say 'Mac-Robertson', and after they'd had their brekkie I decided I'd run them across to the Holy Trinity Sunday School so they wouldn't miss out on their merit stickers. I gave them their collection money and decided I'd wait for them around the corner in the vehicle in Phar Lap Road. Well, they've got some lungs on them some of them. I could hear the kiddies singing with the window up ... hear the pennies dropping.

• *He croons:*

> Sunday school is over,
> And we are going home ...

Beryl had a leg of lamb waiting for us when we got home and seeing as we got the dinner over and done with early I decided to risk it and run them down to Half Moon Bay – just there and back to see how far it was. Wasn't the only one with that idea either, so it eventuated! The traffic was terrific, and the kiddies were like a wagonload of monkeys. By the time I got there and found a decent possie with a view of the beach Wayne got one of his blood noses and the car radio packed up. Marilyn kept grizzling and wanting to get out of the car but I had to draw the line at that. A man doesn't want kiddies carting half the beach through his vehicle and scratching a brand new pair of tartan seat protectors. Besides, I'd had to get out once before, you know, when Wayne wanted to spend a penny. He's really too much of a little man now to go with Beryl and his sister.

Of course, they were overtired and overexcited, so we called it a day and I ran them back to Gallipoli Crescent. They only picked at their tea, and by the time we packed the little scallywags off to bye-byes Beryl and I were almost too fagged to enjoy the instrument.

I was really just as glad that Clive and Glenda were due back on Easter Monday to take the youngsters off our hands because, to tell you the truth, Beryl was beginning to look very peaky and I thought, if this goes on much longer she'll be a cot-case.

I really think you've got to be cut out to cope with children. Not that Wayne and Marilyn were any trouble – we were tickled to bits to have them round the place – but you can have too much of a good thing and they really eat into your time.

One way and another, everything else being equal, and to all intents and purposes, Beryl and I lead a pretty full sort of life and goodness only knows how we'd have managed if we'd ever embarked on a family. Far too busy – that was our trouble. You've got to have a bit of finance behind you too: you can't feed and clothe a family out of thin air. Decent schooling costs a packet in this day and age. Appertaining to

that, Alan Chapman tells me some of the fees they're asking *and getting* are absolutely ridiculous! Further to that, Beryl isn't a terribly well type of person. There's nothing organically wrong with

her – she's never ill – she just isn't a hundred per cent. It strikes me, if you're going to embark on a family you have to take all the particular factors appertaining to it into a certain amount of consideration. Look what happens when they grow up. They either wipe their boots on you, or they marry the first one that comes along and pack you off to a twilight home. I've seen it happen time and time again. You look at these beatniks and juvenile delinquents. When I look at young Wayne and Marilyn I can't help thinking it's a pity they have to grow up.

Clive and Glenda collected the youngsters in the vicinity of seven-thirty. We were all in the lounge room viewing the instrument when the chimes went and they shot to the door like greased lightning. Young Marilyn was clutching the Easter Bunny we'd given her and young Wayne was still wearing a pair of Beryl's high heels, the little Turk! Of course, Clive and Glenda were very appreciative of what we had done but, between you and me, I don't think they realized the half of it.

Anyway, what with all the farewells and good-byes, there was that much pandemonia I forgot to put the tins out.[13]

The place seems quiet without them, of course, but those few days took a lot out of Beryl and, well she got quite weepy when they went. You don't mind doing the neighbourly thing once in a while, but it's nice to get back to your own interests.

• *He acts out an old nursery game, tickling the palm of this left hand with his index finger:*

> Can you keep a secret?
> I don't suppose you can.
> You mustn't laugh
> And you mustn't cry
> But do the best you can.

---

13 • Garbage receptacles. Tin Night is the evening before the scheduled visit by the municipal refuse collector.

Sandy Stone by the author, 1957.

5

SANDY CLAUS

SANDY'S CHRISTMAS RECOLLECTIONS were recited in
my 1965 show *Excuse I*. The monologue was written in London
some weeks before. In order to get myself into the correct rumi-
native frame of mind I used to visit the offices of the Australian
Consolidated Press, then in Fleet Street, and take home piles of
Women's Weekly, in those days an excellent and responsible magazine. I would also drop in on the London office of the *Herald and
Weekly Times*. The poet Barrie Reid had years before drawn my
attention to the 'Miranda' pages of the *Weekly Times* where corre-
spondents, many from lonely rural outposts, besought the advice
of the no doubt pseudonymous Miranda on all subjects ranging
from horticulture to gynaecology. These letters seemed to contain
the distillation of all that was poignant and absurd in Australian
life.

It seemed that the childless Sandy and Beryl should enjoy Christmas, as they had Easter, with little Wayne and Marilyn Nettleton. In those far-off days before the perforation of the ozone layer, a Melbourne Christmas coincided with hot, sometimes scorching weather inconceivable today. Because the English found this paradox so risible, I had recorded a very short and rather crude monologue for the British satirical fortnightly *Private Eye*, in which a Sandy-like character performed the traditional Nordic rituals in candent temperatures. 'Sandy Claus' is a serious expansion of the *Private Eye* squib, and during the passage about Dave Cohen a profound hush generally fell on Australian audiences. Perhaps we had not until then fully apprehended that we, who had invented Niceness, could also be very *nicely* anti-Semitic. It was a salutary discovery. (See also the Eckstein episode in 'Sandy Comes Home', page 159.)

The show opened at the Comedy Theatre in Melbourne and later enjoyed a gratifying success at the old Theatre Royal in Sydney. As before, Sandy addressed the audience from his armchair. The texture of the monologue was relieved by several softly played fragments of department-store Christmas carols.

• *Sandy, in dressing gown and slippers, is seated in his armchair.*

ON CHRISTMAS DAY Beryl and my good self usually make a point of having a few folk around for the midday dinner. It's only once a year

so we like to go to a certain amount of trouble.
Beryl could go on cooking till the cows come
home; and as she always says, she doesn't mind
how much she cooks as long as people eat it up.
Waste not want not as they say in the classics.
Anyway, last year she went crazy. My wife is
known for her puff pastry and she turned out a
batch of five dozen little mince pies and one big
one to keep her hand in. She always gets her plum
pudding over and done with early in the piece
these days too, ever since the year she fell in. I did
my bit too, boiling the sixpences — wouldn't want
the kiddies to get tummy trouble — but my main
department was the tree and the decorations,
etcetera.

CHRISTMAS PUDDING

Cream Copha, sugar and eggs. Add fruit to flour, etc.,
and mix well. Boil 6 hours.

1lb COPHA	quarter pint Rum
1lb Brown Sugar	half lb Breadcrumbs
9 Eggs	half lb Plain Flour
1lb Currants	1 teaspoon Nutmeg
1lb Saltanas	1 teaspoon Spice
half lb Raisins	3 teaspoon Bicarbonate of Soda

We always get our tree from
Bob May, a very nice chappie I know who runs his
conveyance up to the Dandies[1] every Christmas

1 • Hypocorism for the Dandenong Ranges, an idyllic spot outside Melbourne, Victoria,
studded with picturesque hamlets, Devonshire tearooms and pyromaniacs.

and procures them from one of the new reforesta-
tion plantations in the vicinity of the Sylvan Dam.
At night. Naturally I don't quibble. I just say thank
you very much and leave it at that. Mind you, if
I'd known where he got them it'd be an entirely
different proposition altogether.

Anyway, by the time I'd finished with it the tree
look liked fairy-land. I put about four to five
bricks in the jardiniere to keep it firm so the cot-
ton wool wouldn't fall off and we kept the venetians well closed to stop the blessed thing dropping all over the shop before the big day. Pine
needles play merry hell with Beryl's appliance.

Our dining-room table is very deceptive. In
fact, all our furniture is deceptive, but it seats
quite a fair complement with the leaf in, so we
took the opportunity of inviting Mr and Mrs
Simpson, Clive and Valda Clissold, and the
Nettleton couple with their two delightful kiddies,
Wayne and Marilyn, making eight counting Beryl
and my good self. Beryl said the kiddies could sit
at the bridge table[2] and have their *own* little
Christmas dinner.

Well, on Christmas morning it looked as if we
were in for a real scorcher, so Beryl got up early to

---

2 • A folding table with a green baize top, frequently a trap for kiddies' fingers.

pit the dates and do the stuffing before it got too hot to do a hand's turn. I toddled out to give the shrubs a drink before the neighbours woke up and dobbed me in.[3] I toddled off to Communion at Holy Trinity, and the Reverend Polkinghorn, a very go-ahead young chappie, told the men folk they could take their coats off if they were so desirous of doing so. Thats about all I can remember him saying ... must have dropped off. Oh, he commented that he was sorry there weren't more young people at the Carols by Candlelight service but how can you expect kiddies to sit still in church till about half past ten waiting for it to get dark enough for them to light the blessed candles? I just don't think it's feasible. He also said he was sorry there weren't any bells this year, but apparently the Louisa Hutchinson[4] Memorial Speaker System was on the blink. When I got back from church Beryl had given the home a good going over with the Flytox[5] so we wouldn't have to race the blowies to our dinner. The flyspray's on the blink – washer's gone so Beryl has to hold it at a funny angle so the Flytox doesn't trickle down her

---

3 • Australian municipal councils offer generous financial inducements to citizens who betray neighbours violating water restrictions.

4 • (1888–1937) A much memorialized Melbourne philanthropist.

5 • A dependable insecticide.

wrist and get under her ring, with the resultant consequence that she's knocked out all the flies on the skirting board. And she'd even looked out her precious Cries of London dinner mats.

I tried on my Father Christmas costume again but I still had a certain amount of strife with the beard. Beryl had made it herself with pipe cleaners and wadding stitched on to one of her old surgical stockings, but the blessed thing kept slipping off one of my ears and coming away at the side so

that somehow it didn't look real. However, Beryl said when the time came she'd do something with a Band-aid.

Well, the people started arriving before we knew where we were so I handed round the mince pies and a drop of sherry for those who partook. We didn't go to the fag of serving the sherries with an olive on a toothpick because it isn't everybody's cup of tea; besides, Beryl's found the vast majority are just as happy with a pickled onion. Valda Clissold said that she liked sherry but that sherry didn't like her, and I must say the lass looked rather on the peaky side. Beryl said later she thought her whites were very discoloured. Apparently she'd been a bit car-sick on the way over. She's always had that trouble and they've tried everything: Buicks, Chevrolets, Fords, Pontiacs, Hudsons – the lot, but Clive is still very pushed to get her to the nature strip in time.

Alan and Elaine Hotchkiss popped in unexpectedly for a few minutes with some presents and Beryl slipped into the bedroom and wrapped up some Yardley's talcum powder, Potter & Moore's bath salts and a lovely cake of Mornay French Fern *soap-on-a-rope*, so they would never have known.

Alan's quite an identity in the sporting sphere; he's the pro at the Yarradale Golf Club and he told me that latterly he'd been placed in an exceptionally embarrassing position. Apparently he'd been down at the junction the other day and he'd run into Dave Cohen who owns Miss Gretta Gowns of Caulfield, Camberwell and Clayton. Anyway, Cohen asked Alan if he could pull a few strings and get him into the golf club. Dearie me. Now we've all known Cohie for donkey's years; as a matter of fact, Beryl and I can remember when they came over here before the War without a razoo[6] and they couldn't hardly speak the King's English – not that they tried very hard. He's a very *fair* chappie, but Beryl said looking at *her* you could pick it. Not that I hold that against them; heavens alive, it's a free country and what's the old saying? If you shake your family tree one's bound to fall out. And there's no gainsaying they've produced some wonderful people: scientists, musicians, giving money to hospitals and that type of thing. Still he put Alan Hotchkiss in a beggar of a position. I mean, as Alan said to me, if you let one in then you've got to let the rest in, and before you know where you are they're running the whole blessed show. Personally speaking, I wouldn't have any objection if they started up their own club. It's not that they're that short. And as Beryl said the other day, and it's so true, 'Have you ever seen a poor one?' Well, Alan got out of it somehow, but he reckoned that

THERE IS AN INDOMITABLE SPIRIT TO THE EMPIRE WHICH BRINGS, AMONG OTHER THINGS, CEREBOS TABLE SALT TO ALL COUNTRIES UNDER THE BRITISH FLAG

---

6 • A very small sum of money.

kind of thing always happens when you get too pally. Give 'em an inch and they take a mile.

Anyway, when the Hotchkisses had vamoosed the wife said, 'Dinner's ready when you are', so I turned on the fairy lights.

To cut a long story short they fused everything

in the place, including the new eye-level roastmaster, so by the time the menfolk had fiddled around with the fuse box we didn't sit down till a quarter past four and the turkey was as tough as Old Nick. On top of that I couldn't get the pudding to light and when it finally did the plastic holly melted giving it a rather funny taste. Vi Simpson said it was luscious all the same, and anyway it was really the thought that counted. After the roast I noticed that Beryl gave Mrs Simpson a big second helping of potatoes and dickie bird, even though she'd said she'd had an elegant sufficiency. Later on Beryl told me she'd only done it because on the odd occasion we've eaten at their place Vi Simpson had been a bit of an Ikey Mo.[7]

On top of the pudding Beryl had made a

7 • A person of the Hebrew faith, Jewish. (derog). A skinflint.

delicious fruit salad which she'd put in the big cut-crystal bowl she keeps for best. She's had it for years now but it's still got the Dunklings[8] sticker on it. However, everyone was full up to dolly's wax[9] and I was absolutely stonkered, so unfortunately it was hardly touched and Beryl said it was a wicked shame after all the fag she'd gone to. With the exception of the banana, which goes brown overnight, she'd preserved every bit of that fruit herself in her Fowlers Vacola[10] and I can vouch for it personally. Beryl's been bottling all her married life.

The crackers were a bit of a disappointment though. There's not the workmanship in them like there used to be, and we got them all screwed up trying to make them go bang. Clive Clissold said there was a special

– and think of the Saving too!

AUTOMATICALLY THE BOTTLES SEAL THEMSELVES

ED. WILDE

Above we illustrate the popular No. 7 Outfit, complete with 24 Bottles (1 filled with Fruit), Book of instructions, etc.

Price £3/3/-

Plus Freight to Country.

GIVE HER ONE FOR XMAS

Bottled Fruit at Lowest Cost!

YOU CAN EFFECT 100 PER CENT. SAVING BY BOTTLING FRUIT IN YOUR OWN HOME NOW, AGAINST BUYING TINNED FRUIT LATER ON. The thousands of women using the Fowler method will tell you that it eliminates all risk of failure, and that they would not be without it.

FOWLERS "VACOLA"
FRUIT & VEGETABLE BOTTLING OUTFITS

---

8 • A venerable Melbourne (and Perth) purveyor of wedding presents and gems.

9 • Or pussy's bow. Replete, filled with enough food and drink to reach the point at which the wooden or rag body of a doll joins its waxen neck.

10 • Apparatus popular during the inter-bellum period for the preservation of fruit and vegetables.

way of holding them but in the end we had to take the strips of cardboard out and pull *them,* which isn't quite the same. My joke was: Q. When is a door not a door? A. When it's ajar, which is terrifically funny because I got exactly the same joke last year. Beryl said she hadn't seen the joke the Nettleton couple got but she thought it might have been a bit unnecessary.

Then the wife passed round her home-made hedgehog[11] and Turkish delight, but Valda Clissold said thanks all the same but she'd leave it for Mr Manners. I slipped into the bedroom and got into my Father Christmas get-up and when I came out I was the cynosure of all eyes. You should have seen the expression on young Wayne and Marilyn; they thought I was just ... Christmas.

Well I gave out all the presents and Beryl and I did very nicely too, though Beryl said later she was pretty positive the talc Vi Simpson gave her was wrapped in exactly the same paper she'd wrapped

---

11 • Hedgehog Recipe

1/4 lb butter (125 grams)
2/3 cup of castor sugar
2 tablespoons cocoa
2 tablespoons coconut
1 egg beaten (large)
3/4 cup of chopped walnuts and
    optional glacé cherries (mixed)
1/2 teaspoon vanilla
2 cups broken sweet biscuits (180 grams)

Method
1 Melt butter and sugar
2 Remove from heat and stir in coconut
    and egg
3 Add walnuts (cherries) and vanilla
4 Sir in biscuit pieces and mix well
5 Press into greased slab pan and chill
6 Ice with chocolate glace icing and
    sprinkle with chopped walnuts

CUT INTO FINGERS (Makes 24)

Vi's present in last year. In fact, next year she's going to put it to the test. *She's going to mark the paper.* Put a little squiggle on it with one of those new Biro ball points they are advertising in the paper. A bit of a flash in the pan nine-day-wonder if you ask me. They reckon you can write under water with them. But what silly galoot would want to do a stupid thing like that? I suppose if you drowned yourself you could always leave a note of explanation.

Beryl is now a member of the ladies section of the Glen Iris RSL and Citizen's Bowling Club and I gave her a beautiful bowls

box with two bowls which the chappie at the Melbourne Sports Depot said I could change because I wasn't sure of her bias. It was a lovely thing in polished Tasmanian hardwood; actually, it was really a piece of furniture. She gave me a box of initialled Pyramid hankies which were much appreciated. Unfortunately, as it eventuated, there'd been a run on my particular initial but she was lucky enough to procure the nearest one to it.

Beryl's quite right when she says I'm very hard to buy for.

Be that as it may, Wayne and Marilyn had had a very good innings at the dinner table so we sent them on to the back lawn with their presents and the poor little devils wanted to hop into their togs[12] then and there and play under the sprinkler, but their mother put her foot down and told them they weren't to go near water until their dinner settled. Beryl passed round her own homemade date and cashew fudge and we all sat down in front of the instrument and watched the Queen's speech and the bushfire warnings. Then I thought we all ought to get together and tell a few ghost stories around the electric fan, but nobody knew any. Beryl said something funny had once happened to her when she was a toddler, but she couldn't remember what.

Soon people had to be going, and there was still a great swag of perfectly good tucker going begging. Beryl made up a little parcel for the Nettletons to drop into the Louisa Hutchinson Home for Handicapped Kiddies on their way home. They'd only put it down in the drive for a few minutes to gather up the small fry, and Clive

---

12 • Bathing attire. Bathers, swimming trunks, togs, cozzie: affectionate diminutive for woollen bathing attire, often manufactured by Jantzen.

Clissold backed his Packard right over the blessed lot. Still, what the eye don't see the heart doesn't grieve over as they say in the classics. By twenty past six they had all gone to their respective homes, but Beryl likes to see people off; she likes to stand on the nature strip holding a screwed up hankie in the air, roughly in the direction of a receding vehicle. Sometimes she's out there for hours; forgets why she's there. Passing motorists must be a bit surprised seeing her just standing there with a hankie in the twilight. I suppose they think 'what a nice lady, but we didn't have tea at her place!' I told Beryl to toddle off to bed and get a bit of shuteye or she'd be an absolute cot-case on Boxing Day. I said, 'Toddle off and get a bit of shuteye, Beryl, or you'll be a cot-case on Boxing Day.' And she was. I pottered round for a bit cleaning the place up so that Beryl wouldn't have to face it in the morning, but to tell you the truth I felt like a wet rag.

A very hot north wind had blown up again and I could hear people laughing way off up at the Jeffries' place. It rattled the venetians and blew the majority of the cards off the mantelpiece. It's funny you know, we didn't get nearly as many cards back as last year and it was the first time

Beryl could remember Barry and Shirley Bedge-good missing. I knew that latterly they'd had their fair share of bereavement, but as Beryl said, things are never so bad you can't put pen to paper. You'd be amazed the number of friends who sent us the same UNICEF card we sent them. Wouldn't you think people'd have a bit more imagination?

When I finally got into the cot, I switched off the bedlamp and lay there for a while listening to the Bakelite cooling down. Some nights it's more interesting than others. I suppose it was excitement, plus all that rich food, but she was yapping away ninety to the dozen and laughing and crying. Yes, crying a bit and I think she reckoned it was Christmas and she was a nipper. I tried to remember a bit of it so I could tease her next morning, but when I woke up I'd forgotten the blessed lot.

When I told Beryl she said she'd slept like a log and not to talk a lot of twaddle.[13]

It's funny though, isn't it, the way you can't remember your dreams?

---

13 • Nonsense, tommyrot, fiddlesticks, hoo-ha (obs. until revived by Margaret Whitlam).

6

SANDY'S STONE

THE DETERIORATION OF SANDY'S HEALTH was recorded in this monologue of 1968. Although there were frequent references to the Repatriation Hospital, I could never be quite sure which war if any Sandy had served in (*vide* Appendix B). Like many Anzac Day revellers of today, his military status is nebulous. He seemed then too old to have taken part in the Second World War and somehow too much a creature of the thirties and forties to be an Anzac, so I didn't trouble to be too specific on this. No one ever asked awkward questions, although his life and 'mythology' were by this time becoming more and more intricate. This monologue was presented to an English audience on the stage of the Fortune Theatre in *Just A Show* directed by Eleanor Fazan in 1968 where it met with a bewildered critical response.

• *Sandy is discovered seated in a wheelchair beside his bed in a hospital ward.*

I'VE JUST HAD a little op.

The good people here at the Repat have been particularly decent to me for the duration of my stay here, with particular reference to Nurse Younghusband who has been a real tower of strength: a really bonzer little lass; nothing too much trouble. When I first went into the Blamey Ward she said to me, 'My buzzer's there to be used', and I must say she's never turned a hair, though for the first few days I nearly buzzed her silly.

Of course a lot of different ones expect you to know the ropes straight off. When I first came into the ward some little madam put her head around the screens first thing after brekkie and said, 'Yes or no?'

Well, I mean a man's in a strange place with strange womenfolk coming and going; it's not like your own home by any manner of means.

'Yes *and* no,' I said

Mind you, I have never enjoyed a day's illness in my life apart from a few little funny turns that

Beryl couldn't put her finger on. I toddled off to Doctor Hamilton at the time and he couldn't put his finger on it either so this little issue came as quite a surprise to Beryl and my good self. Doctor Hamilton said it wasn't a bit unusual at my time of life and that the vast majority of chappies went through it. He said that as far as Beryl and I were concerned it wouldn't make any difference *whatsoever* to our married life. He hit the nail on the head there all right.

Beryl pops in, bless her, every day around three-ish to eat the grapes and give me all the latest news which is more than some of the other wives do in the Blamey Ward. There's a poor old beggar over there with more holes in him than a pin cushion whose good lady only comes in on Saturday arvos to listen to the races on his earphones.

He's as deaf as a post anyway so I suppose it's six of one and half dozen of the other.

I'm a bit more mobile now but it's no picnic lying flat on your back talking to a loved one and hoping to cripes your locker's shut. I always ask for the screens when Beryl's here. It's not that we get that personal, but you don't want different ones craning their necks to see what a man's wife's got in her stringie![1] I lost a whole box of Sanitarium crystallized fruit that way.

Of course when you're on the sick list you really find out who your friends are. People have been absolutely *marvellous* and ever since I've been in the Blamey Ward I've been showered with confectionery, reading matter and floral tributes. The other day Valda Clissold popped in briefly because she was double parked. She brought me a gorgeous bunch of poppies. Now, most of the other invalids only get glads or carnies[2] or gypsophila. Valda must have really put her thinking cap on. But then in fact, most of the chappies in this ward have got gypsophila – if they only knew it. As luck would have it Nurse Younghusband was off duty that day and some other little madam forgot to burn the stems. Still it's the thought that counts, isn't it, and I really must scribble Valda a little line when I'm back on my feet. Trouble is when you're on the sick list everything's a fag. Do you know I've been in here a whole week now and I haven't once unzipped my compendium?[3]

Doctor Hamilton says I'll have to take it a bit

1 • Stringbag, a once universal hold-all.

2 • Carnations.

3 • A portable letter-writing kit, usually opening and closing with a zip.

easy when I'm back on my feet and I'm giving a certain amount of serious consideration to the retirement factor. When a man gets to my time of life he really ought to start thinking of number one for a change. Of course a lot of chappies retire and they don't know what to do with themselves! Old Jim Fleming from the Buying Department was a case in point. He was busting to retire – reckoned on putting in a bit more time up at their little shack at Kalorama[4] – and though his wife was almost bedridden she still had her own teeth. Anyway when the time came we all clubbed together and put in for a standard lamp and a lovely Bakelite smoker's companion and he passed away two weeks later.

Well that's not *my* idea of retirement.

But old Jim didn't have enough interests. Beryl and I have got our time cut out with the garden as it is though it's gone pretty much to the pack since last summer and Beryl can't do much since she copped that nasty dose of bucket back[5] last February. When the liquidambar died I'd never seen her so upset since she got the news about

---

4 • A rhododendron-invested hamlet in the Dandenong Ranges.

5 • A painful lumbar condition induced by carrying heavy weights, little known in Europe; particularly prevalent during water restrictions. A genuine complaint, as opposed to Turkish (or Mediterranean) back, Greek whiplash, accident.

Tyrone Power.

Now she's only got the silver birch and Stewart Grainger.

Then again I don't want to let my bowls slip.

There's a particularly decent crowd of chappies round at the Louisa Hutchinson Memorial Bowling Green and a man makes a lot of contacts that way. Not that I suppose I'll need contacts exactly when I retire … more friends I suppose you'd say.

Of course Beryl and I used to be as keen as mustard in the old days of the tennis club before the war. Beryl was a little humdinger[6] in the mixed doubles and she always ran up the best tennis cake.[7] We used to sit there after a match with our Thermos with some of the different other couples and their Thermi – and some nights dancing or Crazy Whist.

I'll never forget the night Beryl and I won the Lucky Spot and a pound box of chocolates. Beryl popped them in the new sequinned evening bag she'd made herself – she's always been very good with fiddly things – and she was that excited she forgot all about them until after we'd done the Pride of Erin and she dived for a hankie to blot

---

6 • A fine example of its species.

7 • A cake baked by a female participant in a tennis tournament as a contribution to the hosts' *après-tennis* refreshments.

BLACK MAGIC*
FINE DARK CHOCOLATES BY ROWNTREE

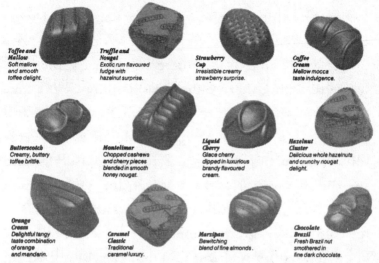

Toffee and Mallow
Soft mallow and smooth toffee delight.

Truffle and Nougat
Exotic rum flavoured fudge with hazelnut surprise.

Strawberry Cup
Irresistible creamy strawberry surprise.

Coffee Cream
Mellow mocca taste indulgence.

Butterscotch
Creamy, buttery toffee brittle.

Montelimar
Chopped cashews and cherry pieces blended in smooth honey nougat.

Liquid Cherry
Glacé cherry dipped in luxurious brandy flavoured cream.

Hazelnut Cluster
Delicious whole hazelnuts and crunchy nougat delight.

Orange Cream
Delightful tangy taste combination of orange and mandarin.

Caramel Classic
Traditional caramel luxury.

Marzipan
Bewitching blend of fine almonds.

Chocolate Brazil
Fresh Brazil nut smothered in fine dark chocolate.

her lip and before you could say 'Jack Robertson' she was up to her wrist in Black Magic. That was a long time ago and the couples have all moved to different neighbourhoods, and then the war. But somehow it always seems afternoon when you're playing mixed doubles ...

There's a tennis club right next to the Repat outside my window and I can hear them playing right up until the light goes and the couples laughing when there's nothing particularly funny and the sprinkler on the spare court and the couples saying 'thank you' to the kiddies when the ball lobs over the fence and I can hear them shut the

Cyclone gate and the cicadas and the different cars going off into the distance.

A funny thing happened when Beryl and I were courting. We went down to Lake Wendouree for a picnic with some of the different other couples and we were sitting there billing and cooing by the lake looking at the view not saying much – closish but not close – and I let my hand slide along the grass till my little finger was just touching Beryl's and she didn't move it and we stayed for what seemed like donkey's years till it got dark and I could feel me old ticker going ninety to the dozen and I knew it was the real thing. Then Beryl jumped up laughing with the different other couples and I could still feel the burning feeling on her little finger and I looked down and saw my hand was touching the blessed Thermos. Had been for an hour and a half. I didn't mess around much after that.

A funny thing. We went back to Lake Wendouree a few Saturdays ago for the first time since our courting days just prior to my hospitalization but I hardly recognized the place. The gardens had changed out of all proportion since the days when the billing and cooing couples used to go there. Lolly papers all over the shop! Everything looked little. Too many amenities. There was an inconvenient amount of conveniences. Beryl had packed a Thermos and a few bits and pieces but it was that blowy the tartan[8] rug wouldn't stay down. In the end, when I got all the burrs out of my socks, I said, 'Let's call it a day' when lo and behold a gust of wind blew a piece of Beryl's greaseproof paper way off to billyho. I said, 'Wait on,[9] forget it' but no, Beryl said she didn't care what other people did, she wasn't going to be a grub[10] and a litterbug and she certainly wasn't going home with a lunchwrap on her conscience.

Anyway to cut a long story short she jumped up and chased the blessed thing over a few of the gravel paths and miniature flower beds and before you could say 'Jack Robertson' she'd tripped over the big hand and stopped the floral clock. Silly place to put the blessed thing anyway. I mean, it'd only have to turn twelve suddenly and cut a kiddie in half!

Of course parents these days let their tinies wander off all over the shop and get into all kinds

---

8 • Doubtless of the famous brand Onkaparinga, a superior make of wollen blanket, named after a South Australian river.

9 • An archaic imperative still current in Australia and overlooked by the Australian post-Barry Mackenzie lexicography industry.

10 • A slatternly person.

of strife. Young Wayne and Marilyn are angels by comparison. A few weekends ago prior to this blessed op Clive and Glenda Nettleton dropped their youngsters Wayne and Marilyn into us at Kia Ora, Gallipoli Crescent while they toddled over to Tassie for a couple of days for Cherylene Cheeseman's wedding. Beryl and I'd said 'any time' and Clive and Glenda know their youngsters are as safe as houses with us. I'm particularly good with toddlers and on the last morning at brekkie I pretended not to notice while Beryl popped an empty eggshell upside-down in my egg-cup and was surprised to find no googie egg[11] inside. You could have knocked me over with a feather. 'Hey Beryl,' I said, 'take a look at this. This googie's empty!'

But Wayne and Marilyn didn't crack a smile. They must have seen that one before. They're an ungrateful little lot these days. That's why Beryl and I thank our lucky stars we never had second thoughts about adoption. It is a bit of a lottery isn't it? And you hear of some funny stories.

There's a couple that we know – let's call them Bill and Joan for argument's sake – no, better call them A and B. Bill and Joan's their name. Anyway A and B tried *everything* and in the end they filled

11 • Baby-talk for egg, especially boiled.

in the requisite forms and got a bonzer little kiddie. Well believe it or believe it not they had a
family of their own after that!

See what I mean?

And you can't send them back can you?

Sister Frizell says I ought to be pottering about
in a day or two and I can't say I'll be sorry. It's no
picnic lying flat on your back between strange
sheets particularly if you're partial to the odd milk
arrowroot.[12] Nurse Younghusband always sweeps
out my crumbs for me when she's on duty but you
can't ask any little madam to do a personal thing
like that, and biscuit burn can be very serious.

I'll give that lass a
little something when
I'm back on my feet.
I've already asked
Sister to make a few
inquiries but Jocelyn
Younghusband's a bit
like my Beryl – she's
got everything that
opens and shuts.

Then again I don't
want to leave Beryl on

12 • A delicious and soluble biscuit.

her ownsome for too much longer. She's a hand-some woman and Kia Ora gets a bit on the quiet side naturally when you're on your ownsome.

Of course Beryl's got the TV but she can't bear to look at the instrument without someone to talk to.

She *says* that she's got her hands full running around like a scalded cat but when she popped in today with a few *Digest*s, a change of jamas and a box of Callard and Bowser's dessert nougat with the edible rice paper I could see she was cracking Hardy.

I only hope and pray that when the time eventually does come – *and it will* – Beryl's the first to go.

It was different in the old days of the Tennis Club and mixed doubles and the Crazy Whist and the couples. But you can't win the Lucky Spot all your life.

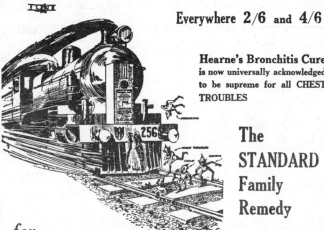

7

THE LAND OF THE LIVING

IN AN ANTHOLOGY PRODUCTION of 1971 called *A Load of Olde Stuffe* I made my first attempt to kill Sandy Stone off. Instead of the customary armchair, the set consisted of a large double bed with a pink candlewick spread, bedside table and Bakelite reading lamp. Sandy enters from stage left after turning off a rather noisy television set in the wings. After a lot of business with light switches, glasses of water and analgesic powders, he falls asleep, wakes up, turns on the light and then reads aloud a series of letters to his absent wife. A lighting modulation between these letters suggests the passing of time. After the penultimate epistle there is a blackout during which a recording of the last letter (Gweneth Longmire's) is broadcast to the theatre audience through amplifiers in the auditorium.

By the early 1970s most Australians were finding difficulty in discerning the borderline between reality and the fictitious world of TV soap opera. Sandy's hospitalization (a period word) had addicted him to a number of programmes which he continued to view avidly or, in his own phrase, 'religiously'. *General Hospital*, understandably, seems to have been his favourite. The fascination which hospitals exert upon Melbourne citizens cannot be overemphasized. The Victorian capital has at least one hospital in *every* street, and it is quite common for people to visit hospitals on Sunday afternoons whether or not they are acquainted with an inmate. Only Intensive Care has so far closed its doors to these processions of the morbidly curious, though there is strong pressure on them to expose their hapless patients to the public gaze.

Sandy also subscribes to the Australian cult of the TV 'Personality'. It must be remembered that we invented the turf 'Identity' who has been largely displaced by the small band of comperes, link men, commentators and stooges who have since attained, due to relentless promotion in the media, the status of demi-gods.

I am pleased to say that this sketch always had a profoundly depressing effect upon those who saw it.

Kia Ora,

36 Gallipoli Crescent,

Glen Iris.

Monday

DEAR BERYL,

My Milo[1] has just caught. This is just a note to let you know I'm still in the land of the living. I was tickled to bits to get your postcard from the Panama Canal. By the time this letter reaches you you will be in the Old Country. I do hope you found your sea legs.

I am sending this care of the bank to be on the safe side. The other day I popped into our little branch of the Wales[2] and had a yarn with Ron Fisher the new manager who took over from poor old Col Lucas. Only a young blighter but one of nature's gentlemen. He was the chappie in shorts who didn't mind when you signed all your

---

1 • A nourishing and sedative chocolate beverage.

2 • The Bank of New South Wales, the oldest commerical bank in Australia, which has since changed its name, with American advice, to Westpac which sounds like something you ask for quietly in a chemist shop when there are no other customers about. It is understood that other names seriously considered for this bank were Whitpac, Packerpac and Wransac.

traveller's cheques in the wrong place.

Well, apparently the Wales sent him over the water for a couple of years in '65 and he intimated to me that most of the different ones collected their bits and pieces at the West End branch of Sackville Street.[3] He reckoned all you have to do is sail in and turn right past some chairs and tables with *Walkabouts*[4] and Bullies[5] on them and there's the visitors' counter staring you straight in the face. Ron reckoned if it was a dog it would bite you. He worked there and he said a lot of different ones ask for their letters at the inquiries or from one of the tellers so I thought I'll hop in first and let you know to save yourself the fag trying to collect

in the afternoon Marjorie brought over her baby boy aged 9 months What a darling and so strong Imagine my surprise when she told me that he had some Vegemite every day. "Why you silly" she said Vegemite is just marvellous for children over 7 months because it's full of That Vitamin B which babies must have to keep them growing steadily

3 · Gone.

4 · A defunct journal given to ethnic affairs.

5 · Copies of the *Bulletin*, a slowly improving Sydney-based journal.

this from the wrong counter. You never know, Beryl, you might just strike some new lass who doesn't know the ropes and go home thinking I never put pen to paper, so better to be sure than sorry as they say in the classics. Ron Fisher reckoned there used to be a lady in the tourist department called Miss Beresford so ask for her if she's still there and she'll give you this letter. He said to remember him to Vonnie Beresford if she's still in the land of the living, but not to bother yourself if she isn't.

Things at Gallipoli Crescent are just the same and I'm pottering round on my own very nicely thanks to your list. I think of you every time I look at the back of the kitchen door. So far touch wood I haven't missed the tins or forgotten to defrost the Silent Knight,[6] although it cost me a phone call and a couple of notes before they cut us down to half a pint and stopped the *Women's Weekly*.

Everyone is asking after you. The other day when I was watering the indoor shrubs and giving your mother-in-law's tongue a drink, who should pop in without a by your leave but Nora Manly. The poor old thing returned that half a cup of castor sugar she'd borrowed before Christmas, and

---

6 • A model of refrigerator popular prior to the invention of the self-defrosting fridge.

she looked so peaky I didn't have the heart to tell her she'd returned it three times already. Besides, I knew she just wanted to have a bit of a peer around the place while you were away, and I've always felt a bit sorry for her since Phil strained his valve. The poor old beggar hasn't any interests and all he does is pick at his tucker and potter round their brand new unit[7] like a blessed ghost. Nora said it was a pity we both couldn't have gone on the *Women's Weekly* World Discovery Tour together, so I told her it's not what you want to do in this life but what you can afford to do; money doesn't grow on trees. Besides, I've got quite enough on the home front to keep me out of mischief and a man can't leave his garden to look after itself. You remember when Bryce Macfarlane went with his lady wife on a trip they came back to a blessed jungle, and Stella said, never again. I've had quite a few of my meals over at the Longmires lately. She'd said *anytime* and they've really been most hospitable and made me feel very much at home. The other night they asked me over to view *BP Pick-a-Box*[8] on their set though

---

7 • Australian flat or apartment.

8 • A once popular quiz show, in which sucessful participants were excitedly urged by the studio audience – and the radio audience – to choose 'the money or the box!'

they don't get the picture we do between you and me. You'll be sorry to hear that Bob and Dolly[9] are retiring although they still look marvellous. Jack Longmire told me Bob was on one of the shows latterly with a nice letter they'd had from the BP people thanking them for everything they'd done but Dolly had to read it because it gave him a lump in his throat. However, Beryl, you'll be thrilled to hear they won the Logie Award[10] and they'll be doing some special bits and pieces for BP. Bob will be doing a lot more fishing too. Won't that be nice?

Gwen Longmire served up a very nice little loin of lamb which was very much appreciated, though you'll be pleased to know she doesn't get her potatoes like you do. She was tickled to bits because her sister Elsbeth, the one with the handicapped kiddie, was over at Southlands last Tuesday and thought she saw Happy Hammond[11] in the distance. It was an amazing coincidence really because she was in town the other day catching a

---

9 • The Surfer's Paradise-based American hillbilly singer Bob Dyer and his wife Dolly (c.1956)

10 • A much coveted statuette in the manner of Barbara Hepworth given frequently by the Australian television industry to itself for superlative excellence in this and all fields.

11 • An Australian television celebrity.

sale and saw a chappie who was the living image of Stuart Wagstaff,[12] side on. She said if he hadn't

been selling lingerie she would have sworn it was

___

12 • A very nice and accomplished English émigré actor who became an Australian TV celebrity through a series of Bensons and Hedges cigarette commercials in which he successfully impersonated an English sophisticate.

him on the Bible. Anyway she got his autograph just in case. Isn't it a small world?

Talking of personalities, I've been watching our shows religiously. In *General Hospital*, Angie has had her baby, but she's putting the little mite up for adoption. It's their lives I suppose. Also, Beryl, you'll be glad to know that in *Days of Our Lives* Tommy wasn't a traitor after all, but a Russian General only told him that to keep him in Russia.

Well, Beryl, that's just about all the news of interest at the moment. Billy Boy is as lively as a cricket and can just about say 'Billy Boy want a cuppa tea' in a funny kind of voice. I laughed. I pop in a fresh slice of granny[13] every day and I've just given his swing a wipe and his mirror a bit of a lick and a promise in case he gets lonely. Birds do so they say. My Old Trouble is taking care of itself and I've been religious with Dr Searle's suppositories. Better to be sure than sorry. Look after yourself, Beryl, and send me the odd snap.

Your ever loving,

Sandy.

P.S. The Avon lady called and said the spray-on deodorant was on special this week.

---

13 • Granny Smith apple.

Kia Ora,
36 Gallipoli Crescent,
Glen Iris.

Wednesday

DEAR BERYL,

You'll be pleased to hear I'm wearing a clean change of jarms. I was thrilled to get your post-card and sorry the smell was so bad, darling. Just a note from me this time to let you know I'm still in the land of the living. Everyone is asking about you and Ron Fisher the new bank manager who took over when poor old Col Lucas passed on asks to be remembered to Vonnie Beresford in London if she's still in the land of living. He's a particularly nice type of chappie. One of nature's gentlemen.

The other night I had a meal over at the Longmires and Gwennie turned on a delicious loin. They'd both said anytime and made me feel very much at home. Gwen's loins aren't a patch on yours though, Beryl, you'll be pleased to hear though naturally I kept my own counsel. As they say in the classics, never bite the hand that feeds you. After the sweets we viewed *BP Pick-a-Box* and you'll be sorry to hear Bob and Dolly are calling it a day. They've had a very good innings but Bob said they would still be making a few BP bits and pieces to keep their hand in, so I don't think we've seen the last of them by any stretch of the imagination.

I was giving your mother-in-law's tongue a drink this afternoon when who should pop in but Nora Manly to return the loan of a cup of castor sugar. She looked done in what with poor old Phil a cot-case since he strained his valve. Apparently all the beggar does is potter round that brand new unit like a blessed ghost. A man needs an interest.

Nora said it was a pity we both couldn't have gone on the *Women's Weekly* World Discovery together so I said fiddlesticks. Money doesn't grow on trees.

I've been watching our shows religiously. In *General Hospital* Angie has signed the papers for adoption and the father now wants to marry her but it's too late to keep the baby. Angie said no and turned him down flat. In *Days of Our Lives* Tom is still suffering from amnesia and he can't remember his wife and family. When he met his daughter he was very emotional. Laura has had a threatened miscarriage which might solve her problem. The baby she's expecting isn't Mickey's, her husband, but Bill's, her brother-in-law. You remember he raped her. In *Peyton Place* Betty and Rod are remarrying. Baby Kelly wasn't Alison's, it was Jill Smith's, and now Connie and Elliott realize that Alison will never come home. They're moving from Peyton Place with the baby. I'm not watching *Coronation Street* because you can pick up the threads of that in London.

There isn't much more news.

I polished Billy Boy's mirror today and he said Billy Boy wants a cuppa tea. He's an intelligent little beggar. So far touch wood I haven't missed the tins or forgotten to defrost the Silent Knight, thanks to your list. Also, Beryl darling, I've sprinkled the Harpic[14] religiously.

That reminds me. You know Happy Hammond? Well Gwen's sister Elsbeth saw him at

---

14 • A sanitary imperative.

Southlands the other day and lo and behold if she didn't run into a chappie who was the living image of Stuart Wagstaff when she was in town catching a sale. It made her day. My old trouble is clearing up nicely thanks to Dr Searle's suppositories. Look after yourself and send me the odd snap.

Your ever loving,

Sandy.

P.S. The friendly Electrolux man called this morning. He seemed very friendly.

Kia Ora,
36 Gallipoli Cres,
Glen Iris.

Friday

DEAR BERYL,

Just a note to let you know I'm in the land of the living. I'm wearing the aqua jarms you gave me for Father's Day. Much appreciated, dear. Things on the home front are much of a muchness and Billy

Boy can say Billy Boy wants a cup of tea. I've given his mirror a lick and a promise. They get lonely so they say. Nora Manly popped in today to borrow a cup of castor sugar. I was watering your mother-in-law's tongue. Apparently Phil just potters around their unit like a ghost since he strained his valve. It's a pity he never joined the bowling club. He would have been sorely missed.

I had a delightful roast at the Longmires this evening. Gwen had said anytime but they don't get the picture we do. However, they'll still be doing a few bits and pieces for BP so every cloud's got a silver lining. You'll be interested to hear Gwen saw Stuart at Southlands today. He was that close if he was a dog he would have bitten her.

Angie is still very upset about having her kiddie adopted, but there could be strife ahead as she knows the names of the adopting parents. The baby, by the by, was a girl who Angie called Jessie after the head nurse at the hospital. Jessie's former husband has returned from South America and it looked as if he was a bit previous in wanting a divorce as he is jealous of Jessie's boyfriend who was the solicitor who handled her divorce. In *Days of Our Lives* Linda didn't lose the baby. She's now convinced that as Mickey is sterile because of the

mumps this is the only kiddie she will be able to give him. However, Mickey is so excited with the news that he tells the family before Laura has time to explain the situation to Dr Horton who is naturally very surprised because he knows the inside story of Mickey's mumps.

Meanwhile Martin Peyton has gone into a twilight home for the last time. Stephen, Betty's ex-husband, is particularly upset about Betty's remarriage but goes to the service much to everyone's embarrassment. The Reverend's wife is now making eyes at Stephen who hasn't exactly said no, and the Reverend, one of nature's gentlemen, is most attracted to his new secretary Jill Smith who is Kelly's mother. Kelly's father is Joey, Dr Rossie's brother.

I haven't forgotten to stop the *Women's Weekly*

or defrost the Silent Knight. Also, Beryl darling, I'm using Dr Searle's suppositories religiously. Look after yourself and send me the odd snap.

Your ever loving,

Sandy.

P.S. The Harpic is cleansing while I sleep.

P.P.S. Clive and Valda Clissold, Mr and Mrs Manly, Tom and Cheryl Kerr, Bill Lesley, the Matthews, the Simpsons and old Miss Warner would all like to be remembered.

Unit 3
Kanangra,
7 Gallipoli Cres.
Glen Iris

DEAR BERYL,

Jack and myself were shocked to hear of Alexander's sudden passing last week. He popped over for a meal about a fortnight ago and seemed as lively as a cricket on that occasion. I'd said 'anytime' and he appeared to thoroughly enjoy my loin and the rest of the meal generally. If I recall aright we enjoyed *Homicide* together and he was most concerned that Detective Inspector Fox and Detective Senior Sergeant Mackay were retiring before your return from the *Women's Weekly*. He seemed particularly worried that you might land back in the middle of a crime wave.

When Dr Searle phoned I asked if there was anything we could do but apparently he passed on very quietly in his sleep. You'll be relieved to hear he *was* wearing a clean change of pyjamas.

I don't know your plans but Jack has been watering your mother-in-law's tongue religiously and I am minding Billy Boy. He can now say Billy

Boy wants a cuppa tea, you'll be pleased to hear.

I saw Nora Manly this morning. She popped in to borrow a cup of castor sugar and sends her condolences. Poor old Phil is feeling the humidity like us all and I'm afraid I don't think he'll be long in the land of the living, but then sometimes they do linger on, don't they?

Please let me know if there's anything we can do. Jack stopped your bread. He joins with me in sending deepest sympathy in your bereavement.

Sincerely yours,

Gweneth Longmire

The dead are creatures of habit'

– Ambrose Bierce

8

SANDY AND THE SANDMAN

'I have heard, but not believed, the spirits

of the dead may walk again.'

(Exit, pursued by a bear)

Antigonus

HAVING KILLED SANDY STONE in 1971, I decided that when he next appeared it would have to be in Purgatory or at least in some ambiguous zone where he might even suppose himself to be still alive. The character was always something of a revenant, even at his sprightliest. The Limbo Sandy inhabits here was furnished once again with a solitary armchair.

'Sandy and the Sandman' was performed in my show *At Least You Can Say You've Seen It* which was produced by Clyde Packer and opened at the Elizabethan Theatre in Newtown, Sydney, on

25 June 1974. I made a very short colour film of Sandy walking towards the camera, stooping to deposit a milk bottle and then retreating into the darkness, waving enigmatically like a dream character in an Ingmar Bergman film. The film was directed by Bruce Beresford and filmed by Don McAlpine.

Sandy herein refers to the snails in his letterbox, a recurring image and one which has a peculiar piquancy for Melbourne audiences, whose letterboxes are to this day, for all I know, the preferred habitation of these popular molluscs (*vide* 'Snails in the Letterbox', a now exceedingly rare pamphlet published by BH, Multiple Sclerosis Press, 1957).

At the end of the sketch the film was projected on to the fuscous curtains beside Sandy's chair, producing a ghostly effect, particularly when the filmed Sandy flickeringly turned and waved in the direction of his more substantial *doppelgänger*.

•*Off-stage sound of a radio in the house next door to Sandy's. ABC radio news theme music.*

I JUST HAD a horrible dream. I dreamed I dropped off the twig. I dreamed I was on my ownsome one night in a place just like our home, Kia Ora, 36 Gallipoli Crescent. It was the same as our place, only different in a funny kind of way; like places are in dreams. I don't think my wife Beryl was in this dream because I kept poking around looking for her and calling out and that. Anyway I couldn't have been *that* concerned because I got into my jamas and hopped into the cot. I've done that on more than one occasion when Beryl has been late home on a Thursday night after chinwagging with some of the different other wives down at the Louisa Hutchinson Memorial Creative Leisure Centre, where she's doing a combined evening course in ikebana, pottery, origami, driftwood jewellery and jazz ballet. My wife has certainly got a lot on her plate on a Thursday night.

Anyway, my head no sooner hit the pillow when I remembered the bottles. Up I hopped again, into my dressing gown, and out into the kitchen. The milk bottles have always invariably been my department and I like to make sure that they're nicely rinsed out before I pop them out by the front gate. Last Christmas our milko told me some hair-raising stories about young couples and New Australians[1] who are sheer grubs when it boils down to their bottles. I know that they get another thorough going-over down at the Glen Iris branch of the O-So-Pure Devonlea Dairies but I don't want to take any chances with *our*

1 • Migrants of Australian or Asian origin.

family's health and you just have to pick up your paper these days to know that sterilization isn't foolproof. Not by a long shot.

My wife Beryl is at the present period of time enjoying the amenities of the *Women's Weekly* World Discovery Tour and if her last aerogramme is anything to go on it's everything and more than the TV commercials crack it up to be. Quite a nice type of experience. Of course, it's no picnic for me holding the fort here at Kia Ora, Gallipoli Crescent, on my ownsome but I hope I can cope as well as the next man.

This morning I toddled down to our front gate to look in the letterbox to see if there was anything there other than snails to ascertain if Beryl had

ALRIGHT MUSSO
WITH YOUR FLEET IN THE BAYS
WE'VE LESS TROUBLES THAN YOU
WE CAN STILL GET OUR 'GREYS' !

THE GREYS
READY RUBBED
MILK CUT
VIRGINIA TOBACCO

Greys is Great

managed to scribble me a little line from gay Paree, where she is at the present period of time, enjoying the amenities. My wife isn't a great one for unzipping her compendium and putting pen to paper so I was pretty philosophical about my chances of receiving one of Beryl's very welcome aerogrammes. There's a dear old friend and neighbour of ours, Les Bullock, a Returned man who was until latterly a purchasing officer with the Electricity Commission. Now a few years ago, old Les had a wife on one of the *Women's Weekly*s and she used to send him *three cassettes a week* religiously, though in Les's case I think he would have appreciated the occasional postcard, because for the last ten years he's been as deaf as a post – ever since he had his wax drained by that Indian locum. Anyway, he used to be tickled pink to get one of Thelma's cassettes and he used to pop them all up on the mantelpiece – just as if they *were* postcards – and knowing as how my little friends Wayne and Marilyn Nettleton are avid stamp collectors, he used to boil the cassettes in the Birko[2] to get the stamps off. Peel them off, and pass them on to me – there's no doubt about it, the Bullocks have always been exceptionally thoughtful folk.

Anyway, I went down to our letterbox this morning, fully expecting to be disappointed, pretty philosophical about my chances of receiving a very welcome communication from the lady wife, when who should I bump slap-bang into but our postman with a smile all over his face. Our postie is an exceptionally nice little chappie. He is a Returned man and he's a cut about a lot of the young whippersnappers in the postal service these days too, with hair halfway down their backs and no whistles. They bung something in your box and ride on past without so much as saying boo. Not our postman. He was rummaging through a great big bundle of letters this morning, and with a real little twinkle in his eye he said to me, 'Nobody loves you today!' It was just a common little courtesy that cost him nothing and it hit the nail right on the head.

As far as I am concerned when a chappie is

2 • A metal jug, fitted with an electrical element.

battling on his ownsome without his womenfolk in the immediate vicinity the first thing he's inclined to let slip are his jamas. The front of mine is as *stiff as a board* – with Milo. I hope I couldn't be regarded as being a grub but I always enjoy a mug of something hot in bed before shuteye. The trouble is I'm inclined to fill the blessed thing up too full with the resultant consequence that by the time I've given it a bit of a stir, propped myself up in bed and unstuck the blessed beaker from the top of the bedside table table I get half of it down the front of my winceyette jim-jams, and all over my Onkaparinga.[3] There's nothing worse than hot Milo on a man's Onkaparinga.

Some chappies' womenfolk skedaddle – toddle off – only for a few days perhaps, and they let themselves go to pack completely. I hope I couldn't be regarded as being such a type of grub and at the moment I've got three pairs of night attire soaking out the back in Beryl's yellow plastic bucket with a good old sprinkle of Bio-Ad.[4] The Milo stains are coming out very very nicely indeed. But those little enzymes are certainly taking their time over the Vegemite.[5] So many

3 • An exemplary blanket.

4 • A powerful yet gentle detergent.

5 • A celebrated yeast-based condiment.

chappies I know, once their womenfolk are on holidays, they get round the home like the wild man from Borneo.[6] The wild man from Borneo! They let the dishes pile up in the kitchen, they bung the tea leaves in the sink, instead of toddling out the back and emptying them on the maidenhair or in the gully trap,[7] or on the lemon tree. Burnt toast crusts and cigarette butts in the old grapefruit skins. Scrambled egg and honey all over the tassles on their dressing gowns and horrible old Kleenexes scrunched up in the bottom of their beds.

I'm reminded of a very dear old friend of ours, Pat Hennessy, a Returned man. Now a few years ago old Pat Hennessy had occasion to bury his wife. After that his teeth never left the bedside table and I went around there one night for a glass of ale and

---

6 • A fabulous Oceanic tatterdemalion with whom unkempt Australian children were often unfavourably compared.

7• A popular exterior cement sink, particularly common in Victoria, for dejecting tea leaves and replenishing watering cans. Also used for extinguishing burning Mallee Roots prior to retiring.

a chinwag with the poor old devil and as the night wore on I had occasion to negotiate his bathroom. That man's S-bend was literally screaming for a vanity brush. If ever an S-bend screamed for a vanity brush it was the Hennessy S-bend. I only hope when Beryl comes home from this *Women's Weekly* jaunt she doesn't find I've turned into a grub; or a wild man from Borneo! Cleanliness costs you nothing and I hope I go to my eternal rest in a pair of passable Exactos.[8]

I had a delightful morning this morning. I went down to the Coles New World Supermarket to pick up a few of life's little necessities and while I was down the shops I had occasion to poke my nose around the corner of the Holy Trinity Opportunity Shop for a bit of a browse. And there in our old opportunity shop, amongst the old tea cosies and hatpins and Scottie-dog brooches, and old Thermos flasks, floral hats and chenille dressing gowns and chipped seventy-eight records, torn pianola rolls and the Hotpoint pop-up toasters on the blink and busted Hecla Boilo jugs and old Astor TVs and thatched cottage teapots, and lettuce-leaf cake dishes with the little chipped tomatoes up one end and old rusty jaffle irons[9]

8 • A well-known and reliable brand of vests (singlets) and night attire.

9 • A hinged bivalve metal device universally employed *temp.* 1950s for toasting sandwiches.

and voluntary helpers – practically anything you'd want – there in our old opportunity shop were a couple of those old-fashioned family snapshot albums. The old snapshot albums like we used to have before the war with the dark brown pages, crinkly covers and like a little silky dressing-gown cord holding them together. And the little fancy corners on the snaps. Old brown faded snaps they were – of families on the beach and picnics up the Dandies at Kallista and Kalorama and Emerald, and Belgrave and Ferny Creek and Sassafras and Cockatoo ... And there were snaps of senior citizens with white whiskers and big knots in their ties and First War diggers, with the gaiters some of them, and the feathers in their hats standing on front porches with the sort of far-away look on their faces like they *knew* they was never coming back. And I couldn't help feeling a bit sorry for all those people all those years ago getting all spruced up and waiting for the birdie, grabbing hold of the kiddies, waiting until everyone was smiling at once and trying not to look into the sun. They wouldn't have bothered, would they, if they'd known they was all going to end up kicking around an opportunity shop with '15 cents' in chalk scribbled across the happiest days of their lives.

We used to have colossal size families back in the old days, big families, whereas today in the present day and age the contemporary tendency is, by and large, for the modern-style family unit to be, to all intents and purposes, considerably on the smallish side. My wife Beryl and my good self, for instance, we ... haven't got any kiddies at all. And I think we've spared ourselves a dickens of a lot of heartache. You pick up your paper and you read some terrible yarns about kids and what they inflict on the people who bring them into the world, pay their fees, cut their lunches and try to do the right thing; *try* to give them a few of the opportunities that they never had themselves. Look at Patty Hearst.[10] Those parents of hers cutting those peanut butter sandwiches day after day just to turn her into an urban guerrilla!

There was a hippie we knew — his dad was a vestryman at Holy Trinity — he wasn't a Returned man, but he was one of the nicest people you could ever wish to meet. This kid nearly killed his father by putting his head in a gas oven. His *own* head, that is; not his dad's. They got him out all right and Doctor Goldsmith, the psychologist up at the Louisa Hutchinson Clinic, he diagnosed it

---

10 • A notorious affluent abductee of the sixties.

as a 'cry for help'. That kid must have really been a brick short of a load ... I mean, if you're going to cry for help, you don't put your head in the stove. You'd stick it out the window, wouldn't you? My heart goes out to that hippie's parents. How could you describe an incident of that nature to the trades people?[11] Bloody little ratbag.

It would be three years now – all of three years – since old Pat Hennessy cashed in his chips. It's a pity he never joined the Bowling Club. He would have been sorely missed. A dickens of a lot of my mates – good old mates – have caught the ferry; just between Gallipoli Crescent here and A.V. Jennings Avenue.

I'm a Mason. As a matter of fact my friends, little Wayne and Marilyn Nettleton, are always at me to teach them the secret Masonic handshake, but naturally I would not divulge. But the Lodge intrigues kiddies: kiddies are intrigued by the Lodge. It stands to reason – a hundred and fifty men locked in one room with nothing but a trowel and a goat. That *would* seem peculiar, I suppose, to a kiddie. Being a Mason, I always carry a sprig of acacia in my pocket in case of a funeral: I can divulge that. That many funerals in my book these

---

11 • Commercial operatives, treated with condescension by middle-class Australians, who obliged them to use the side, back, or tradesmen's entrance.

days, I've just about denuded the bush – I'll be sneaking in the Botanicals[12] at night next! We carry a sprig of acacia and we drop it in the grave-side, or in the casket if the festivities are up at the Springvale cremmie. Not that I have any wish when my time comes to be sprinkled or scattered, or to have my loved ones poking around on a Sunday afternoon trying to find my rose bush, and in the end having to take pot luck. No fear, that'd be a bit like having your snapshot album ending up at the opportunity shop. Or worse, kicking around the tip with the old mattresses and jaffle irons. When I pass on, as I suppose I must, I think the toughest part of all is going to be going Sunday after Sunday after Sunday without a decent roast.

Anyway what am I getting all morbid about? I'm being a silly old sookie[13] – I'm being a silly old sook. Doctor Hamilton reckons my ticker was a hundred per cent when I last went down the clinic and left a bottle. These dreams, *these shock-ers* I have when I go bysie-bye, they're Nature's way of telling me to ease up, taking it a bit more quietly. They'd have to mean something or the sandman wouldn't put them into my head.

I've got a little pal – she's the best kid in the

---

12 • Or Botties, the Royal Botanical Gardens.

13 • A cry baby (etym. obscure).

world – little Valda Clissold. Dear little Valda Clissold, she's a little trimmer. She doesn't forget old Sandy, she's like a daughter to me. She popped in to see me today and she lent me a *Digest* – bless her heart – she'd borrowed from the dentist's and there in this *Digest* was a very informative write-up about dreams and what they mean and another very informative write-up about famous last words like for instance when Doctor Livingstone said Kiss me Hardy, I presume. All of the historical celebrities and olden-days personalities made some little philosophical quip before they jumped the twig. I'm a firm believer that we're all given a little warning we're going to cash in our chips just to give us a chance to rustle up a little speech for posterity. That's how I know for certain that what I had just then – that shocker – was nothing more or less than tantamount to being a nasty dream. A *dream*! I mean if, for argument's sake, I'd been awake and I really *had* jumped the twig, cashed in my chips, kicked off, pegged out, found the road too weary and the hill too steep to climb, fallen asleep in the arms of the Almighty, let the matter drop, or been gathered – if I'd been *gathered* my last words would have been ridiculous. My last words would have been a lot of twaddle and a lot of hoo-ha.

My last words would have been: 'Only half a pint today please, Milko. Money under brick. P.S. Nothing tomorrow'

9

SANDY SOLDIERS ON

THIS SANDY MONOLOGUE appeared in my show *Isn't It Pathetic At His Age* which opened at Her Majesty's Theatre, Sydney, on 13 May 1978 and subsequently ran for nearly two years in both hemispheres. This show was directed by my friend Ian Davidson and I am indebted to him for his help and collaboration on this and other pieces in that production and for changing many lines for the better.

Australia's so-called multicultural character here begins to impinge upon Sandy's hermetic world. It is unlikely that in his earlier incarnations Sandy would have known, or could have pronounced, the name of Ray Stassinopoulos. However, it provides him with an exercise in sibilance as do the opening lines of this monologue; a challenge to anyone with an ill-fitting denture.

This time the set was a bed and a chair with Sandy in his

dressing gown seated in the latter, nursing a hot water bottle. A dim lambency on the bed revealed a large hump beneath the mauve candlewick coverlet.

I AM DECEASED.

With the resultant consequence that there has been a considerable change in my life style. I've never had a day's illness in my life so this little set-back came as much as a surprise to me as it did to Beryl, my good wife.

Beryl's always had her heart set on the *Women's Weekly* World Discovery Tour but she kept putting it off: I think deep down she must have known a tragedy like this was on the cards. She was always on at me to tag along with her but I never had the lust to wander. I could never see much percentage in dragging myself up and down the Leaning Tower of Eiffel. I always felt I'd seen as much of the world as I wanted after a little run down to Rosebud or a spin up to the Dandies on a Sunday afternoon to pick up a couple of shrubs.

And look what happened to old Cliff Jennings. His wife was on and on at him to take the big trip – he took the big trip all right, massive coronary occlusion in the middle of the Changing of the Colour. Poor old beggar keeled over. Brand new

Nikon hit the deck – zoom lens, in-camera sound system, the works – they were both a total write-off. The upshot was, they had to fly poor old Cliff's mortal remains back to Australia first class on Cathay Pacific – and he couldn't even avail himself of the free in-flight beverages. Well that's not *my* idea of a holiday.

But it got to the point where I was getting very worried about Beryl. She was looking very peaky and her polyp was playing up. My wife has always had a big polyp problem. She's seen the top polyp man – she's seen one polyp man after another – even toyed with the idea of a polypectomy. In the end I thought the sea breeze on the Jumbo would do her the world of good. Eventually she made up her mind – sprang it on me. I was giving the silver birch a drink at the time and she jumped me from a rhododendron, waving a *Women's Weekly* and saying, 'Sandy, I'm going, I'm actually going!' And she went ...

Of course, there's plenty for me to do on the

home front to keep me out of mischief — there always has been here at Kia Ora, Gallipoli Crescent. What with the garden, the laundry, nipping down to the shops to do the occasional message, topping up the bird bath every night, popping a little blanket over the budgie's cage, checking his cuttlefish, keeping the home lived in, viewing the *Don Lane Show* and departing this life. A pretty tight itinerary even by *Women's Weekly* standards.

Beryl was on her Scandinavian leg when she received Gweneth Longmire's tragic news of my decease. I wrecked Helsinki for Beryl — if ever a man ruined Scandinavia for a loved one it was me. And she could have caught her death rushing out of that sauna as quick as she did.

But I'll never forget the morning my little widow came home as long as I ... I'll never forget the morning Beryl came home. I heard her key in the Yale — I saw her shadow on the front porch through the reeded rippled glass and in she came, plonked down her cases, and when she straightened up her poor little face was as white as a sheet with a mixture of bereavement and jet lag. Of course there she was — in the home we had shared for all those years and she had one thing on her mind naturally, and one thing only. Cuppa tea.

She shot straight down the passage, left into the kitchen and then she saw it. She just froze stiff at the kitchen door staring at it. There it was – in the sink too – under the dripping tap ... *my last Milo mug.* Still with a little bit of Milo skin hanging over the side. There were a few peas in the sink too that I hadn't managed to push down the grating – still green too. Me gone and them still green!

But she's a brave little soldier and she was at the end of her tether so she popped a couple of Vallies[1] and hopped into the nuptial cot for a bit of well-deserved shuteye. Fortunately the ever-thoughtful Valda Clissold had changed my sheets. Not that I disgraced myself at the time of my passing which is more than you can say for poor old Ray Stassinopoulos. Old Ray had his third stroke – the big one, the biggie, and it was a beauty too – right in the middle of *Are You Being Served?* and a brand new advocado shag-pile carpet. He really blotted his copybook! Well, of course, they've had a rug over the spot ever since but you couldn't hide a thing that size with a bit of furniture – and three enormous couches would look silly in the middle of the lounge. Mind you, poor old Ray

---

1 • Hypocorism for valium, a medicament willingly and generously prescribed by all Australian doctors for cot-cases, housewives and teenagers for any ailment, mental or physical.

always had a very dry sense of humour and I bet to this day every time his little widow Althea trips over that rug he wees himself laughing!

In the days prior to and immediately preceding my internment Beryl was like a human dynamo, up to her eyes in paperwork ... putting a rocket under the solicitor and attending to my estate. My wife and I are without issue, to date, so Beryl is to all intents and purposes my sole executrix. She didn't skimp on my insertion either – if ever a man was given a decent long insertion by his wife it was me!

• *He produces a newspaper cutting.*

'**STONE**, ALEXANDER HORACE "SANDY". ON APRIL 7TH, DEVOTED SON OF HORACE (DECEASED) AND ENID (NEE COCKBURN, DECEASED), BELOVED BROTHER OF HECTOR (DECEASED), LANCE (DECEASED), LORNA (DECEASED), PHYLLIS (DECEASED), AND MURIEL (WESTERN AUSTRALIA). MUCH-LOVED HUSBAND OF BERYL EILEEN (NEE PIZZEY), FORMERLY OF KOO-WEE-RUP. AT HIS RESIDENCE, ALONE, SUDDENLY. BRIEF SERVICE 9.30 A.M., APRIL 14TH, SPRINGVALE NECROPOLIS. FAMILY ONLY PLEASE. IN LIEU OF FLOWERS,

KINDLY REMEMBER THE HOLY TRINITY LADIES'
AUXILIARY JAZZ BALLET STEREO SYSTEM APPEAL.

MEMORIES OF YOU I WILL ALWAYS KEEP,
GOD SAW YOU WERE TIRED AND PUT YOU TO SLEEP.'

Needless to say there wasn't much of a turn-up
at the funeral. My wife must have a bit of Scotch
blood in her because she got a few quotes on me
first – she put out tenders – but in the end she settled for a very reasonable little local firm of funeral
directors. Nice vehicle too — burgundy, power
steering, though I think they could have Hoovered
out the back seat. My poor little widow had to go
all the way out to the crematorium up to her
ankles in confetti! Blessed ethnic driver too – a
man doesn't want a Greek at the wheel on his last
trip and they don't go at the reverential pace that
we're used to here: forty miles an hour through
two amber lights and a cripples' crossing. I wasn't
so concerned for myself naturally, but if Beryl
hadn't had her seatbelt on it could have been a
double event.

Beryl's a marvellous little person though. There
she was – sitting in the back seat of the cortege

like Lady Muck whizzing out to the cremmie,[2] her plate full and her cup of grief running over, but she still had the presence of mind to get the driver to pull over outside our local jeweller's shop so she could drop off my watch to get the wristband shortened. Not many women would have thought of that.

In accordance with Beryl's tasteful request there weren't too many out there to see me off. There was only Beryl. And me up to a point. Oh, and Thelma Bullock and the Longmires. And the Nettletons without their kiddies. And Valda — dear Valda Clissold — she was there, bless her heart, a *true* Clissold. And she was terribly upset too, underneath, in all probability. And there was Nurse Young-husband, and Greg Younghusband. Nurse Younghusband's young husband. And there were three very very distressed people at the back of the chapel. I've never seen more distressed-looking people in my life. Turned out they were waiting for the nine forty-five service. Still it was very nice of them to put their heads around the corner. They were not called upon so to do.

Well, after my dignified committal, after the music had stopped, the curtains had closed and

---

2 • Affectionate diminutive for crematorium.

they'd unscrewed the brass handles, we all came back here to Kia Ora, Gallipoli Crescent, for a cup of tea or a sherry for those who partook and a slice of scrumptious quiche[3] which Beryl had had the foresight to order from a spotlessly clean Danish couple[4] who've started up a gold mine near us. And always being one to strike while the iron's hot, she then and there ushered them all into the bedroom laughing and chatting, with their drinks and savouries in their hands, and Beryl flung open my end of the walnut veneer wardrobe and invited them all to have first go at my effects. Well you should have seen them – they were like flies around a honey pot, rummaging around, emptying drawers, chucking stuff off the coat hangers. I've never been so popular in all my ... life. But after a certain amount of humming and hahing they all took their leave empty-handed. However, my tie collection will come in useful tying back Beryl's tomato plants and my shirts and jamas are going to see years of good solid wear and service in the glove box of Beryl's new yellow Mazda.

Well, after she had farewelled my mourners, Beryl put her feet up, took a couple of Vallies – as

3 • A period flan formerly called egg and bacon pie.

4 • Ethnic minorities often gain a footing in Australia via the catering industry (such as The Dutch Biscuit Man, Miss Maud, Mondo De Carne). Vide 'Sandy Comes Home' re the Ecksteins.

prescribed by Doctor Hamilton for her period of grief – when who should stick his head around the corner but Clarrie Lockwood from three doors down the street. I shouldn't speak ill of the living but he's a cheeky beggar – always has been – more front on him than Myers.[5] He plonked himself in my Jason Recliner,[6] polished off the Penfold's[7] and proceeded to overdo the condolences. He took advantage of Beryl's grief and asked her if he could collar my bowling equipment, though he was gracious enough to add the proviso that he would only take it if she was one hundred per cent certain I had no further use for it.

But my Beryl's got her head screwed on the right way. She soon had his number, and in no time at all she had him huffing and puffing around the home, shifting furniture and emptying drawers until you wouldn't recognize the place. Talk about a slave-driver – she even had him out the back, starting up the incinerator.

I've got a little workship at the back of the garage ... I *had* a little workshop. Lovely set of tools, all in good nick. For years now I've been

5 · A Melbourne emporium with an impressive frontage.

6 · An ingenious armchair with a fold-out footrest, adored by oldsters.

7 · A noted Australian vintner, responsible for Royal Purple Para and Royal Reserve, popular vinous beverages.

working on a miniature dolly's chest of drawers in polished Queensland maple — a lovely little job. Must have started that donkey's years ago, about the time Beryl and I thought ... before we saw the specialist. And what a *delightful* chappie that specialist was! Anyway then I thought I'd give this little piece of dolly's furniture to my little goddaughter Marilyn Nettleton – my little daffodil I used to call her. Used to help her up on to the tram every morning with her lunch box. Haven't seen her lately – not for years now – but she's not a kiddie any more, she's at uni doing Third World Studies and living with a beatnik from Koala Lumpah. Not much use for a dolly's chest of drawers. Still, I'd have loved to have finished that little item before the garbos chucked it on the back of their truck.

But I suppose that when you catch the ferry you're bound to leave something on the jetty, some bit of unfinished business. We all leave undone those things which we ought to have done. But there *is* one thing I wish I had achieved before I handed in my marbles and jumped the twig. I could have done it. It was there to be done too. Every morning I woke up full of good intentions – but somehow I kept putting it off and in the end I didn't blessed well do it ... *defrost the fridge!* I mean I thought about it. I was thinking about it the day I passed away, as a matter of fact. That was a funny old day: something's made that day stick in my memory.

I'd gone out early to the shopping centre and bought a beautiful crayfish – I've always been partial to a nice bit of cray. It was frozen stiff so I didn't pop it in the fridge, just left it on the Laminex work surface to thaw. Fate moves in a mysterious way because if it hadn't been for that blessed crustacean sitting there all over the long weekend in the blazing sun, the next-door neighbours might never have broken in and found me.

Now I'm more or less permanently housebound and I see much more of Beryl than I did in the old days before it happened. Matter of fact, the only time I don't see her is when she goes out to the Garden of Rest to see me. I don't know how long she'll keep that up. It's a long haul out to the Necropolis to view my niche for the two of them – and they've bunged my urn so high up the wall, you'd need an extension ladder to pay your respects.

Beryl's moving up to a townhouse at Noosa[8]

---

8 • Noosa Heads: a select Eastern sea-board resort favoured by Gentiles.

soon. Noosa — wherever that is. She's selling up. This place is a bit small for them. I'll miss her too. We do miss people. But Beryl needs a holiday after the terrible shock I gave her ...

• *He has moved to the bed. He stoops over the candlewick hump. Softly he plants a thanatoid osculation on her obscured chops. He straightens up. Beryl sits bolt upright in bed and emits a blood-curdling scream. Sandy is enveloped in ectoplasm.*

10

SOUTH OF THE BORDER

THIS MONOLOGUE was included in the show of 1981, *An Evening's Intercourse*. I had a vision of Sandy having become inseparable from his armchair, inhabiting a vast opportunity shop, and emerging from an enormous pile of junk onstage to address the audience, literally 'coming out of the woodwork'. At the end of the monologue, when Sandy makes reference to the International Year for the Deceased, I had hoped for a chilling *coup de théâtre*, when the doors of gimcrack wardrobes would creak open and the pyjama'd and nightie'd wraiths of forgotten oldsters would shuffle menacingly towards the audience. For financial reasons and also due to the difficulty of persuading senile actors to remain quietly in cupboards for long periods of time, my theatrical opportunity shop was solely haunted by Sandy.

• *An opportunity shop at night. Racks of cast-off frocks and overcoats, superseded television sets,* Readers Digest *Special Offers, early microgroove albums, toast racks, prosthetic devices, tea cosies, gimcrack fifties furniture, gewgaws, kickshaws, and a clutter of heterogeneous bygones reeking of moth repellent and another sourer odour.*

Alexander Horace Stone, a sere man in his late sixties, is wearing maroon winceyette pyjamas under a worn fawn dressing gown, clutching a hot water bottle with a knitted 'afghan' coverlet. He is seated in a comfortable Genoa velvet armchair, decorated with the russet and brown chevrons and trapezoids of an enervated cubism. Beside him stands a smoker's companion, a chrome and Bakelite standard lamp and a candlewick trimmed shade, to the stem of which is affixed an adjustable round Bakelite tray with a chrome ash receptacle.

The headlights of a passing car briefly illuminate the shop. He wakes.

I'M NOT LIVING at home any more. Since my decease, my wife – my widow – Beryl, has decided to put our lovely home, Kia Ora, 36 Gallipoli Crescent, on the market. It was the first really big decision she made on her ownsome and I can't really say she reached it without a certain amount of help and advice from our dear old friend and neighbour, Clarrie Lockwood, who lives at 43 Gallipoli Crescent and who has latterly been giving Beryl a bit of gentle prodding.

The day after my funeral, Clarrie popped up on the front porch in his supportive capacity for a cup of tea, and in no time he was sitting in the lounge room, helping himself to a slice of Beryl's famous passion sponge. He looked across the lounge at my favourite old armchair and he said it gave him the creeps to see it, because if he half closed his eyes, he could just about see me *still sitting in it*, which wasn't too far from the truth in view of the fact that I was. Clarrie said my chair reminded him of a Genoa

"*I take care of my throat by smoking —*

GARRICK FILTER TIP

"*The Scientific Cigarette for Sensitive Throats*"

✶ The Garrick Filter Tip delivers to your throat and palate the pure benefits of an entirely new and different blend of fine Virginia tobaccos (*a Garrick Specialty*).

10-9d. ǀ 20-1'6

And now in handy Pocket Flat 50 Tins
Also Round Airtight 10's

THE GARRICK
CIGARETTES

velvet tombstone, and it's a wonder Beryl didn't get the waterworks, having to run the Hoover round that every day.

Well, in no time they'd heaved it; chucked it on

the back of his immaculate Vanguard Ute,[1] along with my beautiful chrome and Bakelite all-British hand-crafted smoker's companion.[2] It's a beautiful piece of furniture; a farewell gift to me from my colleagues in the buying department at work on the occasion of my retirement. It's always been a bit of a luxury in our house because I'm a non-smoker, but I didn't like to say anything to my workmates. I'd known them all for many, many years and they'd put a lot of thought into the gift.

Still, you can get pretty attached to furniture and furniture can get quite attached to you, which is why we've all ended up here in the Holy Trinity Voluntary Helpers Opportunity Shop. My lamp, my chair, my hottie and me. Of course, it's a big period of adjustment, death, and you do miss your bits and pieces. Luckily, Clarrie Lockwood on Beryl's behalf has been calling past the

NAMCO Pressure Cooking
Safeguards Food Values

Namco pressure cookery is based on the simple principle of cooking food right through with captive steam.
No longer are valuable mineral salts poured down the sink . . . No longer is precious food over-cooked through long and haphazard application of excessive heat.
Namco cookery is FAST. Fish takes ONE MINUTE for example, peas two minutes. Namco cookery is SIMPLICITY ITSELF, and the savings in fuel costs will pay for your Namco many times over.

NAMCO
PRESSURE COOKER

---

1 • Utility truck.

2 • A chrome and Bakelite standard lamp with candlewick trimmed shade, to the stem of which is affixed an adjustable round Bakelite tray with a chrome ash receptacle.

Opp Shop from time to time in his Ute, dropping off the odd bygone from our married life.

The other day he called past with two tea chests full of my left-off effects including the odd wed-

ding present I'd completely forgotten about. There was the cake dish in the shape of a lettuce leaf with a couple of chipped tomatoes up one end. There was a galleon fire-screen, an Aborigine money-box with one arm, an assortment of rabbit jelly moulds and the pianola roll that Beryl bought once when she thought she was going to get a pianola. She always kept it in a drawer in the dining room in case someone came to dinner who could read music. Oh, and the Namco presssure cooker that she was always too frightened to use, ever since the lady next door had to scrape her Beef Stroganoff off the kitchen ceiling.

And then there were some of my Sunday

School prizes: *The Flight of the Heron* by D.K. Broster, *Masterman Ready* by Frederick Marryatt, *The Gorilla Hunters* by R. M. Ballantyne and *Eric or Little by Little* by Dean Farrar. Books I haven't read for ...? Books I haven't read.

Then there was my precious collection of Hawaiian 78 records including 'Drifting and Dreaming' and 'On the Beach at Bali Bali' sung by Felix Mendelssohn and his Hawaiian Serenaders. And there was Beryl's Fowlers Vacola[3] fruit bottling equipment. When we were first married Beryl would bottle anything that moved. But not now. Her bottling days are over and the equipment's on the blink anyway. The elastic bands have all perished and the metal clips for the top of the jars have all rusted. You wouldn't want to put them anywhere near an apricot or a clingstone peach or a loquat or a quince.

Her Aspaxadrene Inhaler is in the Opp Shop now. Beryl used to get a bit snuffly and she sent off once for a thing called an Aspaxadrene Inhaler. You couldn't get them at the chemist, you had to write off for them. There was an ad in the back of the paper, at the back of *The Pix* I think it was, or *The Australasian*, or *Table Talk*, showing an old-

---

3 • Apparatus popular in the inter-bellum period for the preservation of fruit and vegetables.

DON'T ASK YOUR GROCER FOR IT

Ultra Modern Magic, Harmless

ASPAX-ADRENE

(for use only in the Apax Inhalator)

IS DRAMATICALLY EFFECTIVE AGAINST

Asthma, Bronchitis, Hay Fever, all air passage Catarrh, Sinus, Antrum, Polypi, Croup, Whooping Cough and a Preventive against Common Colds and Influenza.

It is an ethical preparation, prescribed by doctors

AND IS OBTAINABLE FROM CHEMISTS ONLY

(and rightly so)

FRUIT FROM THE FRUITERER; GROCERIES FROM THE GROCER; CHEMICALS FROM THE CHEMIST

fashioned kiddie in period clothes gaining intense relief from an Aspaxadrene Inhaler. It was next to another ad that used to intrigue me, which said MARK X FOR YOUR RUPTURE. It was a picture of a bloke's torso with circles all over it. You had to put a cross where your rupture was and then you'd fill in a coupon and send off a postal note and a beautiful truss would come back in the post and no one would know you were ruptured – except the postman.

I once knew an old bloke, a Returned Serviceman,[4] and a delightful chappie. He put a cross in every circle. The postman got a hernia delivering the equipment. He couldn't even lift it on to the verandah. The old boy had to lie down to wear it too. Starved to death.

Anyway, we had to fit this Aspaxadrine Inhaler together. It said, 'Even a child could do it', but we could never find a kiddie to show us how. Then there was the Astor 21-inch TV set that we bought in 1956 to watch the Melbourne Olympic Games. We saw Lorraine Crapp on that. More than once, too, in black and white. As well as Dawn Fraser, Shirley Strickland and Betty Cuthbert.

---

4 • An ex-serviceman or veteran.

And the Morphy-Richards pop-up toaster. The one that once gave Beryl a terrible shock. She was trying to dig out a crumpet with a fork. That's a mug's game. I've always maintained that the Morphy-Richards pop-up toaster people, and the Hoover, Hekla, Hotpoint, Sunbeam, National, General Electric and HMV pop-up fraternity, never took crumpets into account. I don't think they'd ever *seen* a crumpet. You slip one in and half an hour later, if you're lucky, it glides to the surface, white as a lily. I think there's something in the crumpet itself. I once read what was in a crumpet. There's a lot of interesting crumpet literature. It's on the cellophane round the packet, and I read it once, one wet afternoon. Actually, I read it twice. It was that wet. There's soluble solids of crumpet, edible crumpet fats, edible crumpet flavouring – just as well they're all edible – then there's emulsifiers and stabilizers. Goodness knows why a crumpet needs stabilizing. To stop it falling off the plate, I suppose. And then there's niacin, lecithin, riboflavin, trace elements and enzymes. And it's one of these enzymes that neutralizes the electricity in the toaster. I mean, theoretically, if you had enough crumpets, you could black out a city.

But sometimes it has the opposite effect. Flames leaping out of the toaster. You've got to bash it underneath with a broomstick, and then you're on the kitchen floor trying to find it, and over the sink, scraping off the black fur till there's nothing left but a couple of crumpet holes. A black crumpet hole is no use to man nor beast. But there's a little knob on the side of a Morphy-Richards toaster. A tiny little knob, and you could

miss it. And Beryl did. She missed it for years and then, when she found it, she couldn't leave it alone. That's the womenfolk for you. On the left of the knob is the word 'light' and on the right of the knob is the word 'dark' and over the top of the knob is the word 'medium'. The interesting thing about the knob is — *it's not connected to anything.* It's got a mind of its own.

That's when Beryl reached for the fork, thereby making a near fatal mistake. But it beats me that a household appliance *that can't even push up a crumpet* can throw a woman from one side of the kitchen to the other. She went up ... and down. I came in, and she was sitting on the lino with a fork in her hand and a little bit of crum-pet on it, just chat-ting and laughing to herself. The light was swinging too. She must have hit the ceiling. If it

ARNOLD'S
ROTARY CLOTHES LINES

hadn't been for the fly wire door, Beryl could have impaled herself on the rotary clothes hoist.[5] She could have gone head first into the compost tum-bler. Of course, you'd have the police round in a minute, asking awkward questions too. 'Excuse me, sir, what is your late wife doing upside down in the compost tumbler?' What could you say?

5 • A free-standing, revolving metal clothes hoist of umbrella form invented by the Hills Company, Adelaide, which revolutionized the Australian wash day.

'Crumpet did that.' I doubt if they'd buy that. They wouldn't buy that.

Since my cremation, I've kept a pretty low profile. But you'd be amazed the number of people who try to get in touch with you. I never thought of Beryl as a superstitious woman, but the other night, Clive and Valda Clissold came round. The Clissold couple. Well of course I'd known Valda Clissold for years. I knew her when she was a Valda Smoothie, before she was a Clissold because she married into the Clissold family, but there was always something a little bit Clissoldy about her and she came round to offer her condolences to Beryl and Clarrie Lockwood was there, seeing if there was anything he could do, and doing it. Valda, typical Clissold, Valda, suggested a seance; a seance to get in touch with me. So they got out the old card table with the funny leg. The one that once pinched Beryl's thumb. The whole ball of her thumb came up like an emu's egg – purple. It doesn't matter now but it mattered then. It mattered then and not now. That's life for you.

Anyway, once they got the card table up, they put the Scrabble letters all round it, and then they put an old honey glass in the middle. Or a peanut

for lunch outdoors ...excellent!

So satisfying for outdoor appetites! So mellow and delicious! Easily digested... and a complete food. Gives strength and energy for even the most strenuous day. The 8-oz. and 4-oz. cartons or the 1-oz. portions are the most suitable for open air meals. No rind—no waste. Clean and wholesome in its silver-foil wrapping. Easily carried!

KRAFT CHEESE

"Only the finest Cheese is made by Kraft"

HER TASTE IN GOWNS IS EXCLUSIVE ... HER TASTE IN CHEESE IS KRAFT ... IT TAKES A GALLON OF RICH MILK TO MAKE A SINGLE POUND OF KRAFT CHEESE.

butter glass. Or perhaps it was Velveeta. Honey, peanut butter or Velveeta, it doesn't matter. They're all equally psychic. Then they turned off everything except *Copshop*,[6] and Valda put her finger on the glass and said, 'Is anybody there? Is anybody there? Speak to us, Sweet Spirit.' And Clarrie Lockwood put his finger on the glass too, and his knee under the table pressed up against Beryl in a manner which was hardly in keeping with the spirit of the occasion. I've never been more tempted to give that glass a bit of a nudge in all my life. But then I've never believed in the

---

6 • A popular Australian television serial.

occult. I've always thought it was a load of twad-dle, a load of hoo-ha. Mind you, a lot here in the Opportunity Shop, they never get a message from the other side at all. *Nobody's got their finger on the glass for them.*

But lately, Beryl's been like God's gift to the tourist industry. She hasn't stopped travelling. She seemed to get the travel bug the day of my fu-neral, funnily enough. She leaped from the cortege into the Pioneer Parlour coach, up there with all the other bereaved women, laughing and singing (*he sings*),'I'm looking over a four-leafed clover ... tie a yellow ribbon round the ... strangers in the night ... bye-bye blackbird', whizzing through the countryside in the big parlour coach with the coach captain pointing out the points of interest and telling all the ladies how long it would be if you joined everything together and the weight of all the bricks in the Town Hall and the sun streaming into the bus and all those little freckled widows' elbows sticking out the windows with their hubbies' watches glinting on their wrists. But Beryl needs the time and I have all the time in the world.

On most of her trips, Beryl took a pal with her for company, little Gwen Longmire. Little Gwennie's husband, Jack, went to his Reward about two years ago now. Yes, it would be two years since Jack went to his Reward. It would be a good two years. It would be all of two years. It would be all of a good two years. Gwen took it badly too. She wasn't brave like Beryl. Not like Beryl. But then she didn't have Clarrie Lockwood to fall back on.

I could never see what Beryl saw in Clarrie. She used to say he reminded her a bit of Bill Peach[7] on the TV. We're big fans of Bill Peach. He was a bit like Bill without the hair. But boy, we loved it when Bill Peach did that documentary about the Murray River – going up the Murray on the *Murray River Queen*. I was viewing that night and I called Beryl. She was in the kitchen. I said, 'Beryl, Beryl, it's Bill. He's going up the Murray on the *Murray River Queen*.'

And she ran in from the kitchen, drying her hands on a Wild Flowers of Tasmania Irish linen tea towel. She said, 'Yes, it's Bill. He's going up the Murray on the *Murray River Queen*.' I said, 'Yes, I told you he was.' I said, 'That's a trip we've got to do.' And she did.

I had a reservation on another ferry. I had another river to cross. Oh, but she had a lovely

7 • A revered Australian television presenter.

time on the *Murray River Queen*. The food was nice. A few too many Mornays I think was her only criticism. And Beryl likes a Mornay. But there were just a few too many, give or take a Mornay. But they had bingo every night and disco classes for the senior citizens. Medically supervised. And lovely films. They had *Caddy* and *Stormboy* and *The Hanging Picnic Too Far Away* and they stopped at a place on the river bank called Swan Reach and had a barbeque – a barbie – and the Purser dressed up as a bunyip and he chased Gwen into the bushes, nearly ruining her lime green and apricot crimplene pantsuit.

But the highlight of highlights of that trip was the fancy dress dance. Beryl and Gwen went as two jolly swaggies from 'Waltzing Matilda'. Beryl had remembered, luckily, to bring my navy blue double-breasted pin-stripe that she had forgotten to give to the Salvation Army the day after the funeral. And they weren't the only widows either, jitterbugging the night away in the apparel of their deceased loved ones.

But we used to love fancy dress dances in the old days before the war when we were young. I'll never forget one we went to at a place called

8 • A seaside resort in SW Victoria, Australia, now ruined.

Lorne.[8] It was a beautiful spot before the war. Quite a hop, step and a jump but popular with young couples on long weekends. On Saturday nights there would always be a fancy dress dance at Erskine House and a band would come down from Geelong or Colac; one of the top Colac orchestras. *The* top Colac orchestra. And there would be Japanese lanterns up in the trees before there was anything wrong with that. They were like tomatoes, those Jap lanterns up in the trees. I remember saying to Beryl, I said, 'Beryl, look at those lanterns. They're like tomatoes in the trees', and she looked up and she said, 'Yes,' she said, 'they are. They're like tomatoes.' She was always coming out with things like that.

And the young couples would walk along the beach, holding hands, in the old days before you had to remember to hold hands. And in the moonlight the sea was stiff like plasticine, and you'd hear the band in the distance. Well, you wouldn't. You'd hear the drum. You'd have to guess the tune: South of the Border, down Mexico Way ... Give me one dozen roses, put my heart in beside them and send them to the one ... little Sir Echo, how do you do ... hello, Little old lady passing by ... torralooraloorah torraloorah looralayay

... When they begin the ... There's a Rainbow on the River Somewhere Over the Rain ... goodnight sweet ... Quick step, slow fox, quick fox, slow fox, quick fox, slow fox, valeta, pride of Erin ... Beryl went as a Honolulu lady that night in a grass skirt. It took us a fortnight to get the Kiwi off her face. The Solvol[9] did the trick in the end, mixed up with a bit of Bon Ami[10] and Old Dutch cleanser.[11] And I had a brainwave. I put a sheet over my head and I went as a ghost. I put a sign around my neck that said 'ghost' in case someone thought I was a sheik, because there were five sheiks and only one ghost, which was me. And I got the second prize for originality, which gives you an idea of the standard. I think it was a lovely box of Columbine Caramels with a window down the side of the box to show you how many were left. There's no windows in confectionery any more. It might have been a box of Old Gold Assortment or Winning Post, but I don't think so. But it was a long time ago. It was ... before the war. I reckon I'd be a dead cert for the first prize now.

After that, Beryl and Gwen went to New

9 • A pumiceous grey soap no longer favoured.

10 • A favoured scouring agent.

11 • A mildly abrasive white powder used to chase dirt (discontinued).

Zealand to boil an egg in a volcano.[12] A Dickens of a long way to go to do a stupid thing like that. Then they went to England for the Changing of the Colour and Buckminster Castle, Anne Hatherley, all that pomp and pageantry. They bought a Polaroid in Singapore for only a fraction more than they would have paid in Melbourne and there was a bit of my insurance money left, so they did the Pacific Islands. Manila, Suva, Singapore, Bali; they bought every raffia basket in sight. The Abbos couldn't weave them fast enough. *They came back rattan infested.*

But I'm glad I had my Big Trip in my sleep. You see, I wouldn't want to end up in an Eventide Home or a hospital or a Retirement Village or a Sunset Hostel for the Elderly[13] or motel-style accommodation for the bewildered, smelling of chloroform and Brussels sprouts. That's what they smell like to me. Death and roast dinner. Gravy and the grave. You go into one of these hospitals to see your loved one. You know they're not coming home. The sisters tip you the wink. You're sitting on the edge of their bed, trying not to look in their locker, and you're saying, 'No, no, those

---

12 • A therapeutic activitiy recommended to tourists visiting the less stable provinces of New Zealand.

13 • A salubrious terminary.

grapes are for *you*. All right, just one.' You leave them with a few twigs. And you say to them, 'We've kept your lovely room just as you left it.' You've let it to an Asian student but you don't tell them that. And he's bringing his family out next week. And you're looking at them, wondering if they know you know. And they're looking up at you, wondering if you know they know you know. They know, you know. And whatever hospital you're in, if you're in a public ward, three beds down, there's always an old bloke lying flat on his back with his mouth open. And the funny thing is, it's always the same old bloke. I think he's a plant. I think he's put there by some organization. Rent-a-stiff. Something like that. He's the one the sister says *never gets a visitor*. Lucky beggar. He'll get a visitor all right; he'll get the one we all get when the screens go round our beds for the last time. He'll get the visitor who doesn't bring a box of Sanitarium

Crystallized Fruit. But he does bring a box. That punctual old visitor who pops in on us all.

Anyway, you're sitting there on the edge of the bed of someone you've known all their life. And suddenly they're running out of breath. And you, why, you're running out of things to say to them. Nature times it nicely. And you sneak a look at your watch. And they open one eye and see you, and all you can smell is roast pork and crackling and gravy and parsnips and roast pumpkin and crunchy potatoes and apple crumble and custard sauce being wheeled up and down the hospital corridor. You can't be grief-stricken with your mouth watering.

But I wouldn't want to be a misery to myself and a burden to others. That's why I'm very glad and grateful that Beryl and I never had any kiddies … any close relations. You hear terrible stories about kids, bundling their old folks off to homes. Some of them dragged off the bowling green. I've heard that. Dragged kicking and screaming off the bowling green. I heard of one old bloke, a returned Serviceman but a delightful chap, he was delivered to a home by his nephew who he'd *never even met*. One day he was playing bowls with all his mates around him, and suddenly this young fellow in jeans and a kind of T-singlet, with a Cornell Wilde haircut, walks across, looking like a bodgie,[14] or a beatnik or something. He walks across and taps him on the shoulder and says, 'Excuse me, old boy,' he says, 'I'm your nephew. The van's over there.'

This old boy turns up at the home and he's still in his creams with a bowl in his hand. He thought the nursing staff were lady bowlers. Hello, Vi, hello, Elsie, hello, Ernie – Ernie was the matron. Unfortunately, the carpet in the hospital was green and on his first day he crippled a specialist. Well, they took the bowl off him; nearly took his finger off with it. Within a week he's gone – dead! *Not for me.* If I could have my death all over again, I hope I cross the great divide, catch the ferry, jump the twig, I hope I'm gathered, I hope I go to my Reward in the comfort and privacy of my own home. You forget, even we forget.

Property in Glen Iris has gone through the roof. When Beryl and I first built our home after the Depression, Glen Iris was practically the Bush. It was almost Sydney. We were pioneers, Beryl and me. No one thought Australian cities would ever get that big. I mean, where the Crescent is now

---

14 • (fifties slang) An Australian teddy boy or lout.

there was just paddocks and a lavender farm. Funnily enough, when I put in the rotary hoist years ago a little bit of lavender came up in the back yard out of nowhere!

Beryl never liked that hoist; she only had it because all the other womenfolk in the street had one. She missed her old clothes line down the back. Never got used to that rotary hoist. At night, if she came out for the pegs or something, she'd always forget and brain herself on the blessed thing. You could set your watch by her squawk. Then, if she tried to dodge it in the dark, she'd usually get bogged in that part of the lawn where the air raid shelter used to be. Nothing ever grew where we filled that thing in. Of course when you tell kids today that practically every backyard in Australia had an air raid shelter once upon a time they just laugh at you. They don't believe anything ever happened to us, when in point of fact .... *it nearly did.*

I'd get an old tennis ball the dog had finished with, clip a bit out of it, and bung it over the spokes of the hoist. Beryl would just bounce off it. Caught on, that idea of mine too. Swept Australia.

I once said to Beryl, I said, 'If anything happens

to me,' I said, 'there's solid gold under this house.' She must have taken me pretty literally. I'd hardly been sprinkled in the memorial rose garden before Clarrie was under there with a metal detector. All he found was an old Ardath[15] cigarette tin and a rusty trowel some dago brickie must have left there before he was interned.

Oh no, they did find one thing. They found an old snapshot album. One of those old photo albums we used to have, with the dark brown pages and little corners on the snaps. Old faded snaps the colour of tea that you made with condensed milk. I must have stuck it under the house years ago so Beryl wouldn't find it because there's a couple of snaps in it that would have upset her. Pictures of me and a lass from the Sunday School that I used to court before I ever met Beryl. Little Phil Tremlow. She was a goer.[16] I was pretty stuck on her. There were pictures of me and little Phil at Sunday School picnics at Mordialloc[17] and Half Moon Bay and up at the Colin Mackenzie Wildlife Sanctuary, patting wombats. The wombats would be dead now.

But I don't know what happened to Phil. I

15 • A widely enjoyed brand of cork-tipped Virginia cigarette no longer smoked.

16 • An enthusiastic female participant in romantic dalliance.

17 • A charming Melbourne bayside resort.

heard that she married a Rawleigh man[18] and had a lifetime's supply of Ready Relief. And I heard from someone at the Lodge who knew her, or thought he knew her or knew of her or knew of someone who knew of her, or even knew her or thought he did, that she'd had a big family of kids. I'm glad if that's so. She was — we were pretty fond of youngsters. But I lost track of her years ago. It's funny, you lose track of the people you love. People you're fond of. People you hardly know – you see them all the time.

But it was damp under the house. It can get damp under a Glen Iris home. That old snapshot album was swarming with slaters.[19] Clarrie had to carry it to the incinerator on his shovel. It was a beggar to burn; a tin of kero didn't do it. He had to delve into the incinerator with a garden fork, turning the pages and sticking them through ... 1936 ... 1937 ... 1938 ... and we'd put in a few wet afternoons years ago, fixing those snaps, getting them nice.

But he can see himself in a lot of things at my place, Clarrie can. He broke into my shed the

18 • A door-to-door salesman of Rawleigh's (NZ) pharmaceutical and culinary products, no longer ubiquitous.

19 • (Scottish Australian) *Oniscus murarius*. A sub-order of ispod crustacean. Woodlouse with nineteen pairs of appendages. Lives under stones and in damp places, letterboxes, etc. Eats dead wood. Also known as carpenters.

afternoon of the funeral. He didn't ask Beryl for the key, just smashed in the door of the shed, took my tools and I had my name on all of them on a Band-aid. He took the Qualcast mower and the Pope sprinkler, and I'd like a shilling for the number of times I've rotated that sprinkler. And he took the shrubs. Well, I knew he'd been pinching those even when I was sick. I'd hear him, up the side, brushing past the Daphne and ferns at night. He took the erica, the shrimp plant, the malaluka, the paligonia and he's had his eye on Beryl's cumquat for years. But I mustn't speak ill of the living. I just hope and pray that Beryl won't do anything too hasty. And I don't think she will — she wouldn't, she won't. And I wouldn't want to come between them, not that they'd know if I did. I just hope that one day, the League of United Nations will invent an International Year for the Deceased. Then we'll all come into our own.

But the auction is on Sunday. The auction's tomorrow. The old home's been completely stripped. Just squares on the walls where the pictures were. They left the calendar behind the kitchen door, that's all, because its no use to anybody. It's just days and weeks.

Beryl's camped in the spare bedroom. The one

we used to call the nursery. I'm not going back. Never go back. Until she moves into her new condominium at Surfer's Paradise,[20] Beryl has to borrow all the necessities of life from the neighbours. Funnily enough, she's just about to cross the street now with a cup in her hand.

• *The sound of screeching brakes – a thump. After a pause we hear the creaking of a door opening and a shaft of bright light enters Sandy's chamber. He looks up towards the light.*

'Talk of the devil.'

• *The voices of Nelson Eddy and Jeanette McDonald singing 'Ah Sweet Mystery of Life at Last I've Found You', swell to a climax. Sandy walks exultantly into the brightness.*

---

20 • The Lido of Brisbane. A high-rise resort where Schmutter-merchants and Samurai rub shoulders in the sun.

SANDY COMES HOME

HERE, SANDY RAILS politely against the ethnic influx. My own parents' home in Camberwell had recently been purchased by a charming Ukrainian couple so I was unable to bring, as I usually do, a high degree of personal animus to this creation.

The monologue was written very quickly in a Melbourne hotel, though it underwent considerable embellishment on tour, and nearly doubled in length. The show was called *Tears Before Bedtime* (1985). Once again I would thank Neil Munro and Edward Clarke for their felicitous inspirations. This sketch has been filmed by the BBC, a little too cheerfully for the author's taste.

• *A drab room in the process of renovation. Half has already been painted in bright hues of turquoise, coral and canary. A picture of the*

Parthenon on black velvet, tentatively hung. The other, undecorated half of the room is illuminated dimly through a broken wooden venetian blind. There is a fireplace surrounded by tapestry brick, and on the mantelshelf several possessions of a former occupant are still ranged, festooned with cobwebs. A tarnished metal trophy, a damaged elephant bookend, a wooden biscuit barrel, a framed wedding snap, a rusty cigarette tin.

The room is unfurnished except for a lounge chair covered with a dust sheet, a stepladder, paint tin and painting accoutrements, an elaborate child's bassinet draped in nylon tulle, and beside the lounge chair (centre) stands a smoker's companion.

The Cosmopolis couple enter – she very pregnant and bearing a bolt of gaudy fabric – he in paint-splashed clothes, carrying a cassette player blaring bouzouki. She rips the dustsheet off Sandy's chair, revealing its 'invisible' occupant. She holds a length of fabric over Sandy and they stand back to appraise the effect. They seem to approve, gather their things and exit. As the music fades, Sandy wakens and the lamp flickers spookily.

I DIDN'T WANT to come home. Our house, Kia Ora, 36 Gallipoli Crescent, Glen Iris, has been bought by a delightful multicultural ethnic minority Greek couple. At the auction the bidding got pretty fierce, and at one stage we thought our home might be snapped up by a couple of boat people. But in the end the multiculturals won.

Not that you ever have much say as to who's going to live in your house once you've passed away, and by the some token, when you buy an established residence, you can never be sure if the deceased occupant has granted you vacant possession.

But I didn't want to come home ... it's a funny story. After I passed away ... caught the ferry ... jumped the twig ... had my last cup of Milo, my wife – my widow – Beryl, decided to put our home on the market so she could move up to a new unit in a condominium at Surfer's Paradise. Shortly before the auction, Beryl had a nasty fright right outside this house when she was crossing the street to borrow half a cup of sugar. A silly woman in a metallic blue Toyota Celica came out of Ellerslie Street and knocked her for six. It was touch and go for a few hours and Beryl eventually crossed the dividing line, took one look at me, and went straight back to the land of the living. I didn't take it personally. Beryl's got a lot to live for.

She threw a lot of my left-off effects into a couple of tea-chests, dropped them off at the holy Trinity Voluntary Helpers Bring-and-Buy Opportunity Shop along with my favourite armchair. I took it pretty philosophically; Beryl wasn't to know I was still sitting in it. It was originally part of a lovely Paterson's suite – you furnish well at PPL,[1] the firm with a million friends – and we bought it on very reasonable terms many years ago. It used to have little suede stoles over the polished walnut armrests, with ashtrays attached, but being non-smokers they went by the board well before the war. But it was and *is* a glorious piece of furniture and the voluntary helpers at the Opp Shop put a ridiculously low figure on it. (• *He consults ticket*) Fifteen dollars.

I think if Beryl had known the Church of England were going to throw it away for nothing, she would have given it to the Salvation Army and then I might have ended up in a halfway house in Albert Park for disabled lesbian partners without parents. The ladies in the Opp Shop, Miss Hoadley and Mrs Chesterman, refused point blank to take my beautiful chrome and Bakelite

1 • Paterson's Proprietary Limited. A once famous furnisher.

smoker's companion, saying that there was absolutely 'no call' for them in this day and age. Mind you, they were made to last, and most of the companions have outlived the smokers.

Anyway, I can't say how long I was in that Opp Shop window in Burke Avenue, staring out over the car park with a ticket on me that said 'Art Decko'.[2] All I can say is it wasn't art decko when Beryl bought it, and if it *had* been we probably wouldn't have. But one morning, this little Greek mother-to-be, this little Cosmopolis woman came in, fell in love with this chair and had it delivered to her new home, which turned out to be *my old home* ... Kia Ora, 36 Gallipoli Crescent, Glen Iris. It was a chance in a million. Fate moves in a mysterious way.

But I didn't want to come back. The house, the street, everything's changed out of all recognition since the old days before the war when young couples like me and Beryl came to live here. Not that we ever had anything against the occasional multicultural. Beryl always had 'Welcome' on her doormat, but that didn't mean you invited them on to the premises.

I remember before the war, she used to get all

2 • A meretricious Australian decorative style employing chrome and frosted glass, much sought after by antipodean parvenus.

her fruit, all her veggies from a little Chinaman, a little smiling Chinaman by the name of Charlie O'Hoy. Little Mr O'Hoy used to drive his horse and cart religiously once a week from his market garden on the Banyule Estate behind the gasome-

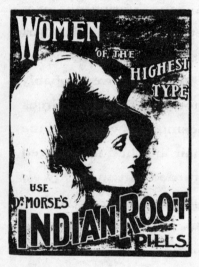

ters at Heidelberg.[3] He'd come up the cutting, round past Ivanhoe and Alphington where the paper mills are today, over the river along by Studley Park, up past the Lunatic Asylum to the T-junction at Cot-ham Road. Then down Glenferrie Road, down the hill past the Methodist Ladies' College on the corner of Barkers Road, over Christobel Crescent, under the railway bridge, along by the Hawthorn Town Hall on the left and then up, over the tramline at Riversdale Road to the top of the hill. Then he'd go down the hill past Scotch College[4] on the right and then left all the way, hard left via Gardiners Creek to Glen Iris. Quite a

---

3 • A Melbourne outer (now inner) suburb, originally a German colony, then a bohemian enclave, later the site of a popular repatriation hospital, in *esse*, *vide* 'Sandy's Stone'.

4 • A Melbourne Presbyterian school famed as a training centre for Real Estate Agents.

long journey for a little Chinaman in a horse and cart. Particularly in view of the fact that sometimes Beryl's only requirement was an onion.

Occasionally Beryl would pop out into the street to his cart, but mostly their business was conducted through the tradesman's hatch down the side. There would be a thump on the servery door and his little yellow hand would come through with a couple of quinces or a punnet of something. Beryl said he had longer fingernails than Myrna Loy,[5] and that Myrna could have taught him a thing or two about cleanliness. She'd always scrub his quinces religiously too; Beryl said you could never be too careful. But there's no doubt about it, he was a cheery little beggar with a lovely smile from ear to ear, and when he died, we read an informative article on him in the *Argus* and it eventuated that that smiling little Chinaman owned half Glenferrie Road!

Another colourful ethnic minority we had a lot of time for was a Russian called Boris with a beard and a knitted hat who used to go round on a bicycle, clipping people's hedges for three-and-six a time. Funnily enough, I bumped into Boris years later at the Camberwell market. He looked exactly

---

5 • Film star. Famed for her long fingernails as the eponymous daughter in *The Mask of Fu Manchu* (1932).

the same and it turned out he originated from Warrnambool and his name was Simpson. Sometimes it can be a real headache picking a foreigner.

A Greek couple had our nearest fish and chip shop, near the junction, with water running down the window and jars of oysters, mussels, Tassie scallops and pickled onions from one end of the counter to the other. On the odd occasion I'd pop in there so that I could surprise Beryl with a few whiting or a nice flattie[6] wrapped up in *Smith's Weekly* or an old *Table Talk*.

Italians were a common sight in our neighbourhood too before the war, and I well remember the Angelo brothers who were terrazzo specialists and did a lot of the front porches in our street. They also did all the crazy paving at the Kendalls', the Whittles' bird bath and the Nettletons' crossover. I can still see the little beggars covered with lime, wearing hats made from Geelong cement bags with their hoses hanging over the edge of a rusty drum. They were always singing, but when war broke out, they disappeared while their terrazzo was still wet. Old Cess Gilchrist had a theory that a lot of dagos who had been Musso[7] sympathizers

---

6 • A hypocorism for flathead, a popular Melbourne fish.

7 • Dimunitive of the name of the one-time Italian trade union leader and author of *The Cardinal's Mistress*, Benito Mussolini.

had been rounded up and interned out near Watsonia. Although Cess was always one for a furphy,[8] we never saw those Ities again.

But the first *real* foreigner to purchase a property in Gallipoli Crescent was a little Israelite called Eckstein who appeared on the scene with his wife round about 1938 and moved into Rivoli, the new ultra-modern block of flats on the corner of Ellerslie Street. They were the first flats we'd seen in our suburb with green cement steps, glass bricks on the stairwell, corner windows and festoon blinds. Not Beryl's taste or mine, but the Ecksteins kept themselves very much to themselves and it wasn't long before they had everything that opens and shuts. Apparently he worked in a chocolate factory in Elsternwick and he ended up owning it – don't they all! She ran a goldmine in the Block Arcade, selling coffee and toasted raisin bread. Beryl said they worked like a couple of niggers and were far too busy to learn the King's English. But the Ecksteins were pretty popular with local kiddies who collected stamps. Apparently they still had a few rellies[9] somewhere on the Continent and some of the letters they got had stamps *with Hitler on them*! But those letters

8 • (A First World War saying) An unreliable rumour.

9 • (dimin.) Relatives.

suddenly stopped ... Little did we know then, all those years ago, that the Eckstein couple were the thin edge of the wedge. Today, the floodgates have opened, and now it's a case of Come One, Come All.

I mean the Stubbings' beautiful home, down there at 52, that's been remodelled from top to bottom by a Vietnamese couple called Ng – from Vietnam. That's their name. NG they spell it ... we thought that they might have shortened it out of consideration for their Australian neighbours – shortened it *to* Ng, that is to say, not *from* Ng. You couldn't do that. Well, you could, I suppose. You could shorten it to 'G' or 'N'. But we were happy to meet them halfway down the road. Well, as far down the road as possible. Then we thought it might have been the first and last letters of something ... like 'nothing'. But you could smell their cooking on the bowling green. Old Phyllis Prescott looked through the fence once and she saw the Ngs sitting on what had been the Stubbings' patio, shelling peas. She said she couldn't believe her eyes. They throw the peas away! They just cook the shells! They throw them on the dustbin lid with a bit of Worcestershire sauce and chuck in anything that moves. So we were very worried when old Miss Warner's Cocker[10] went missing. Luckily it turned up in the dog pound, or those Ngs could have been in hot water. They could have been deported if they'd had passports.

But the first house in the street to actually fall into enemy ... *foreign* hands, was Vi and Alan Chapman's lovely Californian bungalow-style home, just across the road from us at number 37. We'd known Vi and Alan for years. And they were in the tennis club with us before the war and in the bowling club and the Crazy Whist. They were the first people we knew to have an overseas trip in the fifties. The first people that we knew to bring back a *My Fair Lady* record. But latterly they had become rather elderly, in fact we were quite concerned as to how elderly they had become. Their daughter-in-law, Beverley, had been trying to get them into a flat or a unit for some years. That's the main function of a daughter-in-law; getting old people into units. They want us all on the one level; *below ground level* if you ask me. But Vi and Alan wouldn't budge. They clung on until the eleventh hour, until the Death Knock.[11] They were still in the lounge room

---

10 • Spaniel.

11 • (Australian usage) The last minute.

watching *Neighbours* long after the instrument had been disconnected, when the new owner, Bruno Agostino, and his family of eleven had their tea chests and Kelvinator in the driveway.

But of course once they moved in, that once-lovely home was swarming with dagos night and day. Talk about build. They built on the back, they built on the front, they built on the left, they built on the right. They built another storey on that home and they dug underneath, they built under the house itself until that home ended up filling the entire block from the right of way to the front fence. And it would have broken Vi Chapman's heart to see what they did to her porch. They built a balustrade right across the front of the home, with fountains and statues and lions everywhere. It was like a cement safari.

They had a big garage too, more like Preston Motors than a private garage. But they didn't have a boat in the drive ... they had a *ship*. They could've sailed back to Italy in it. Goodness knows where their money came from. Old Cess Gilchrist, who never misses a trick, reckoned the Agostinos had a market garden up Griffith[12] way. You would have thought money grew on trees. They

---

12 • A fertile riverside district in New South Wales where marijuana shrubs are rumoured to be grown.

must have sold up before the bottom dropped out of tomatoes.

But it's what they did to Vi's garden that broke our hearts. I mean they dug the whole blessed thing up with a rotary hoe. Every trace of Vi Chapman's green fingers went by the board and she had a *magnificent* garden. On the front lawn I remember she had a beautiful silver birch and a liquidambar, and a little fish pond with a bit of chicken wire over it to stop the fish getting out. Then round the back they had the lantana over the gully trap and morning glory on the tool shed and the cotoneaster – a magnificent cotoneaster, which Vi sacrificed in 1951 to put in the hoist. Then they had the pittostorum, a magnificent pittostorum, and a pinoak. I can remember when she bought that pinoak as a seedling at a Methodist Church fete years before the war. And it grew into a beautiful tree, *a magnificent tree*. It was a lovely tree even when war broke out and last year it resisted the bulldozer for the best part of a day. In the end, those Ities got the block and tackle to it and it came down with a groan you could hear up and down the crescent. Only when they were chopping it up did they find a little bit of rotten wood nailed on to one of the branches ... all that was left of a tree house that little Neil Chapman had played in *before the war*. Of course, little Neil was beheaded in Borneo. Some Jap with a sword said, 'Neil!', and he did, and that was that. It's terrible to think your destiny can be in your own name.

Anyway, we went out to see Vi and Alan in the unit that their daughter-in-law had so kindly arrranged for them, but by the time we made the trip, poor old Alan had had a major stroke and Vi was blind. Yes, Vi was blind. But Beryl never goes anywhere empty-handed. She had made her a delicious pineapple upside-down cake from a recipe she found on the label of a Golden Circle pineapple tin. Well, she got most of it off the Golden Circle label; there was a bit that stuck to the tin that she never did get. But Beryl used to improvise, in the kitchen at any rate. 'When in doubt – Copha',[13] that was her motto. She loved Copha, she used to swear by it. She first became a Copha User back in the fifties really, when she started making chocolate crackles off the back of a Rice Bubbles packet, and then she fell in love with Copha itself. She started slipping it into everything. Sandwiches, cool drinks, you name it. She

13 • A white shortening agent made from solidified coconut oil and a culinary imperative in the 1950s, especially in the production of chocolate crackles.

said if a kitchen had Copha and borax, it was off to a running start. I wasn't going to argue the toss on that one. I wouldn't buy into that. But it was certainly a beautiful pineapple upside-down cake, and old blind Vi, she knew what it was too, just by the feel of it. She said, 'You've brought me a sticky cake, Beryl.' We were amazed! When you think of all the things it could have been.

Then she asked Beryl a very embarrassing question. Suddenly, out of the blue, she said, 'Beryl?', and Beryl said, 'Yes', and then she said, 'I'm over here, Vi', and Vi said, 'Oh, there you are, Beryl. Are those Ities looking after my beautiful garden?' I've never been more proud of my wife's diplomacy. She gave Vi a long look of reassurance. She said, 'They've certainly taken care of your garden, Vi. *You've got nothing left to worry about there.*'

Down the road, the Longmires' home has been bought by a Chinese couple. The first thing the Chows did was to build the Great Wall of China in front of it. A bluestone[14] fence eight foot high. The neighbours can't seen in anymore. And dear old Doris Morrison, who never used to miss a trick, who invented Neighbourhood Watch, can't see over the fence so she's lost interest in life itself.

14 • Basalt used in the 19th century for the construction of Melbourne's finest villas (demolished in the fifties and sixties of the 20th century).

Dropped her bundle.[15] She even began to neglect her Meals on Wheels. Little casseroles started to pile up on her doorstep. *Just the opportunity her daughter-in-law was waiting for*. She frog-marched Doris into a maximum security Retirement Village. It had all mod cons too, including little buttons on the wall that the old folk could fall against in an emergency – if they were lucky, and their aim was very very good. Of course, they had to police that a bit. If they were alive next day they got fined.

That house was on the market within minutes and the ambulance taking Doris away nearly collided with the cars coming to view the property. There was her daughter-in-law and the Estate Agent (an old Scotch boy) showing people through with the oven still warm from Doris's last batch of scones. Her dripping still hadn't set in the blue striped bowl on the window sill; the damp Kleenex in her nightie pocket under the pillow, her crumbs in the bed, her teeth in the kitchen.

But that home found a willing buyer in Dr Farouk Ben Narsimmon, an Indian doctor, and his wife who worked out at the Uni. Beryl said the

15 • (Australian) Handed in the towel.

wife had the brains, and she had a little red sticker on her forehead. She used to get around in a saki all day long, and she'd always walk four paces behind her hubby. Something to do with their diet. Mind you, if Beryl and I ate nothing but curry, I hope we'd come to some arrangement.

Lois and Theo Gosper! They were a young couple when Beryl and I were young. But they're dead now. After they were relocated by their daughter-in-law, their lovely Spanish Mission-style home at 47 was bought by a Greek. A little chap by the name of Con Skorpios. He pioneered formal dress hire in our neighbourhood. He rents out pale green and mauve ruffled shirts to chappies who want to be married on the bridge in the Botanical Gardens in the rain. There's a shilling in that apparently. Actually he bought the Gospers' house by accident. Well, he had to have about seven or eight accidents[16] before he could afford it, but he's got a big family to support. They're all invalids too, funnily enough. They've all got whiplash injuries. I never thought it was hereditary.

Con Skorpios has bought a few houses in the street on spec, and he's on the Council too. He's

---

16 • In this context, profitable misadventures for the adequately insured.

trying to change the name of our crescent to a Greek name: Parthenon Road or something, but it would be a tragedy to lose a lovely old Australian name like Gallipoli. Anyway, he's let the Gospers' house to some Australian students. In point of fact, they're the only Australians now living in the street. They play the wireless very loud. Just as well that old Ukrainian woman at number 34 who knits on the front porch all in black is deaf as a post!

They don't do much, the students. They don't do anything. They roll their own cigarettes and have door-slamming competitions. Being unemployed, they've all got cars and they park them on Lois Gosper's lawn. I can still see little Lo, before the war, weeding that lawn on her hands and knees with a kitchen knife. Now you wouldn't know there'd been a lawn there. It's a dust bowl.

The students get up in the middle of the night, run out, slam the doors and go back to bed. They're probably on a grant to do that. Could be a bi-centennial project.[17]

They buy all their clothes at the Opportunity Shop too. I've recognized two of my cardigans. And there's a beatnik girl with green pointy hair

17 • Expensive often frivolous refurbishment of the urban and rural amenity during the year 1988 in order to make Australia more convenient for Japanese tourists.

like a cocky and a safety pin in her nose. She's got a kiddie running round with no nappies too, and a safety pin in *her nose*. She wears the suit that I was married in!

But most of the other young couples that we knew are dead. Well, they're not all dead. Some of them are alive, but they're not couples. I mean to say, bits of couples are alive; partial couples. Those who are left are in the units. They don't do much in the units. They stand in the middle of the room on their frames, wondering who they are, where they're going and whether it's worth it. Sometimes they look out the venetians if they're open. Otherwise they look at the venetians. If they're looking at them and they're open, they look out of them and they might catch a glimpse of a bulldozer moving in on their old home, or they might see their laundry

PEOPLE as well as TRAINS, MUST BE REGULAR

— that's why my wife buys FORD PILLS for all our family in the **LARGER** economy, family size

turning into a Jacuzzi.

Old Della Shapcott was looking through the

venetians of her unit once, and saw the wreckers moving into her home. There was a sign on the corner of Gallipoli Crescent, 'Wrecking at number 29', and people came from everywhere, like locusts. They just backed their trucks up over the nature strip and took everything they could get their hands on. The house was a pile of rubble by the time they'd finished, and that hand-weeded nature strip looked like old photos of the Battle of the Somme.

They've built more units there now, but the builder left the old jacaranda tree Della had planted. However, the body corporate of the units had that jackie removed in the end. It kept dropping leaves and blue flowers on the concrete and cars. There's hardly a garden left on Gallipoli Crescent that isn't buried under tons of cement, black plastic, pine chip and pebblecrete.[18]

At number 28, where Doug and Thelma Little-john lived before their daughter-in-law found them a nice compact unit, a Sicilian chappie has put plastic pebbles down over what was left of the garden after they'd added a rumpus room and treble garage. But for a few years afterwards, the old bulbs kept trying to come up through the plas-

---

18 • Increasingly popular substitute for lawn in some of Australia's more Latinized purlieus.

tic: snowdrops, grape hyacinths and a few jonquils. Even the odd freesia tried squeezing up between the plastic and the house. But Reno kept on mowing them until they all finally gave up. I remember Doug used to have lily of the valley thick down the south side of that home, but when a bit of that showed up beside the pebblecrete, they had to have a couple of goes with the Zero[19] to get rid of it.

Dot Swift! Dear old Dot. Fancy forgetting her! Dot Swift was an Identity; a real character. Beryl said Dot had once been a big woman. At one stage I think she was, as I recall, a very big woman. Beryl said that she once took a 42D cup. I never knew what Beryl meant by that. I assumed Dot had once borrowed something and failed to return it, though I never realized Beryl numbered her utensils.

But Dot was born in this neighbourhood. Her people were very comfortable and she was born in a beautiful old home about eight or nine streets up the hill in the old part of Glen Iris. It must have been a magnificent old colonial-style dwelling with views over most of East Malvern.

It had a Norfolk Island pine tree (which you

---

19 • A ruthless and popular herbicide.

could see from the tram stop), a beautiful magnolia and a monkey puzzle tree. It had big, wide verandahs smothered with wisteria, a tennis court, a croquet lawn and a summer house covered with honeysuckle and a love-walk. It was called 'Braeside' and it was in Braeside Avenue too, which I always thought was a coincidence. But it was a magnificent old home; it was like something out of *My Brilliant Picnic Too Far Away*.[20]

Dot spent her girlhood there. She married Wilf, and they came to live in the Crescent when the street was new, with other young couples like me and Beryl, Vi and Alan Chapman, Lois and Theo Gosper, Doug and Thelma Littlejohn, Alf and Della Shapcott, the Dunns, the Greys, the Clarks, the Munros, the Whittles, the Longs, the Braggs ... Warners ... *people with real names*. Later on, Wilf developed an inoperable polyp which proved to be a polyp *and* inoperable. So he got a second opinion and died. Come to think of it, death *is* a second opinion.

Dot didn't stay on her own in Gallipoli Crescent for long, rattling around in that big house like a button in a Bendix.[21] She moved into a small unit on the recommendation of her daughter-in-

---

20 • A classic Australian film of the idyllic school circa 1975, portraying Australians in a favourable and attractive light and therefore popular.

law, and it was a very small unit. The Estate Agent (an old Scotch boy) hit the nail on the head when he described it as a 'deceptively small' unit. It was downstairs at the back of a building but it had everything that opens and shuts. I mean, if you wanted to open something, you had to shut something else. But anyway, as I say, Dot hadn't lived in Braeside, the family home, for years. It hadn't even been in the family. Dot's father had left it to the Church, donkey's years ago. And latterly, in the fifties, the Church sold it to a consortium of doctors who turned it into a private nursing home for the bewildered. It was very popular, too. The bewildered spoke very highly of it. They never advertised, it was just word of mouth. One bewildered person talking to another bewildered person, so that soon the word spread around the entire bewildered community, which is bigger than you'd think. It's *enormous* according to a bewildered spokesman.

But the doctors made some big improvements. Naturally they chopped down all the trees. They chopped down the Norfolk Island and the magnolia and they poisoned the wisteria in case twigs, leaves and petals got in the guttering, and they

---

21 • A brand of electrical washing machine.

bowled down the 85-year-old summer house and they built a magnificent cream brick geriatric wing over the croquet lawn and the love-walk. They even changed its name form 'Braeside' to 'Montcalm', probably because they thought 'Montcalm', would be less bewildering to the bewildered. But kiddies coming home from school, looking for caterpillars in the hedge, could still see the old gate buried there in the dusty privet with the old name still on it.

One morning, Dot was in her unit and she had a bit of a fall. She took a tumble, poor old Dot. As luck would have it, Jocelyn, the daughter-in-law, was there at the time, having a bit of furniture valued. She realized that when old people fall *you don't move them*, so she had a cup of tea and a cigarette. But she couldn't stand the moaning and groaning any longer, so next morning she looked up the Yellow Pages under 'twilight' to see if she could find a facility for old Dot. And she did. The nearest place she could find was a private nursing home about eight or nine streets up the hill in the old part of Glen Iris called 'Montcalm' which had been 'Braeside', *Dot's childhood home*. But I don't think Jossie ever knew that.

So picture old Dot then on the doorstep of

Montcalm with nothing but what she stood up in, or what she'd fallen down in. She still had some family treasures but they were back at the unit. Nothing she could move into one room. Where was her ruby glass? Where was her Credenza?[22] Her cruet? Her solid brass spark arrester and the little tongs and bellows and the little brass shovel and brush that hung on the tapestry brick hearth where many a mallee[23] had crumbled in the winter – where were they? Where was the old Ansonia clock? And the doilies and serviettes that smelt of camphor that had hardly ever been used?

Where were the apostle teaspoons and the mahjong with the pieces missing? Where was the little tin with a bit of her wedding cake in it, hard as rock? Where was her bridal veil, and the framed views of Egypt and the pianola rolls of Floradora, *Chu Chin Chow* and the *Maid of the Mountains*? Jossie made sure Dot was safe in the ambulance before she beckoned the Salvation Army up the drive and lit the incinerator.

So Dot Swift's on the doorstep of Montcalm with a little globite case[24] and not much rattling around in that. Couple of nighties, framed photo

22 • A hideous 'period' sideboard, now mandatory in the homes of Australian accountants and solicitors.

23 • A highly combustible fuel deracinated from the red soil of Victoria's seriously eroded Mallee province.

of Wilf in uniform, a little cracked celluloid soap dish with a thin sliver of Rexona in it. She didn't need much. She was only going in for 'observation'. So they told her. And naturally she doesn't know the big, wide mosaic verandahs where she played as a child, because they're teeming with wheelchairs now. And how could she recognize the big front room where she used to learn the piano as a kiddie. She wouldn't recognize that in a month of Sundays because now it's full of little old ladies with tubes up their noses, all enjoying *Perfect Match*.[25] And by one of the coincidences as only seems to happen in real life, they allocated Dot a room at the back, which had once been her own nursery when she was a child. She doesn't know that either, because rooms get smaller as you get older. And this one really has, because they'd lowered the ceiling and squeezed seven beds in it and she hasn't seen it for sixty-seven ... sixty-eight ... best part of seventy years.

But three days later, when she comes out of sedation, she gets a young nurse to help her to the window. Costs her money, but she does, and when she looks out of that window for the first

---

24• Indigenous Australian luggage sturdily fashioned of dependable compressed fibre.

25 • A popular television entertainment called *Blind Date* in England.

time in sixty-seven ... sixty-eight ... best part of seventy years, she can't believe her eyes because there, still standing, is the old peppercorn tree where her Dad once fixed up a swing. The tree stands in the doctors' car park now, pretty well ring-barked[26] to death by BMWs.

But next morning, the morning nurse, who comes from Sri Lanka and who is as black as your hat, likes a Maxwell House and a king-sized mentholated St Moritz with the physio at eleven, she has a good laugh at Dot's expense. 'You know that new one, that Mrs Swift in 21? She's a real character. *What a character.* Do you know what she does all day long? She just stands at the window, looking at the car park saying, "Where's my swing? Where's my swing?" She think's she's a budgie.'

I'm glad I never had a fall. You just have to trip these days for your daughter-in-law to be into the Yellow Pages. The world is full of elderly citizens lying on the carpet, looking up at their daughters-in-law, saying, 'I didn't fall, I didn't fall. *I like it down here.* I'm just dusting the skirting board.'

I get a lot of letters – I get a lot of mail. It was a fatal day when I filled in that coupon applying for

26 • A method of killing a tree by cutting a complete circle around its trunk.

a *Reader's Digest* special offer. Beryl said at the time, 'You do that,' she said, *'and they'll pursue you beyond the grave.'* And they have. I get six letters a week and I've been dead six years. Beryl gets a big post too, but she never left a forwarding address. She was in too much of a hurry to soak up the sun in her new condominium at Surfer's Paradise. She's Beryl Lockwood now. She married old Clarrie from across the street. I'm glad she did. I wouldn't want her to be lonely. Not living and lonely. And I'd go up there and keep an eye on her too, if the tram went twelve hundred miles. I still like a tram trip. The conductor never asks me for the fare; special concessions for the dead. All night buses are full of us.

But I didn't want to come back. I won't outstay my welcome, I'll just wait until their little one arrives. (• *The bassinet effulges and Sandy looks across at it.*) It's funny that Greek couple turning this dark old spare bedroom into a nursery. Bit of a coincidence really. Beryl and I used to call this room the nursery at one stage of the game. Until we moved in the suitcases and called it the box room. But I'm glad there'll be a kiddie in Kia Ora at last and I'm glad Beryl didn't throw away all my bits and pieces too. She used to call me a bower-bird[27] and a hoarder. She'd say, 'You're a hoarder.' She always had a gift for words. She'd say, 'You can't take it with you', and she certainly didn't.

• *Sandy rises and crosses to the mantelshelf, rummaging amongst its dusty detritus. He blows a skein of cobwebs off a framed photograph.*

She even forgot our old wedding photo. Fancy forgetting our wedding photo. Still, it'll be interesting to the little new arrival; give him an idea what a married couple looked like. There's a lot of my memorabilia still here. Here's the mulga-wood biscuit barrel I won at housie housie at Erskine House, Lorne, in 1938, and my bowls trophy. (*He raises it like Parsifal.*) Valda Clissold, bless her, wanted that as a souvenir of me, and Beryl said she could easily take it down to a little man at the junction and have my name buffed off it, but Valda never came back. Still, there it is in pride of place on the mantelpiece; they love a bit of history on their doorstep. Greeks. (*Sandy examines the sealed cigarette tin, opens it.*)

What's this? A lock of my mother's hair. I thought we'd lost that years ago. Still here!

---

27 • Australian bird of the bird of paradise family which constructs elaborate runs adorned with feathers and hetrogeneous debris.

Cherished by those ethnic minorities. Well, it's a good thing for kiddies to be brought up in a home with a few old bygones in it. We had them when we were young. 'Don't touch that, it's Nanna's,' they'd say. And 'Don't touch that, *that is Nanna*.' She had the *Pictorial Atlas of Australia*. I once looked up the word 'Aborigine'. It said 'original inhabitant'. That'd make Beryl and me a couple of Abbos. So this is my Dreamtime.[28] This is my Sacred Site.

• *Mrs Cosmopolis enters with a brush and plastic dustbin and hurls the objects on the mantelshelf one by one crashing into the bin. She pauses at the cigarette tin, opens it, sniffs its fibrous contents then holds it upside down over the bin and taps it fastidiously as the dusty ringlet of hair dislodges itself and falls for ever into the garbage.*

Well, if that's how they treat a man's memorabilia, *don't give them back the Elgin Marbles.*

• *Slow curtain.*

---

28 • In Aboriginal mythology, the time in which the earth received its present form and in which the patterns and cycles of life and nature were initiated.

12

A LETTER FROM LIMBO

The curtain rises on a bare stage revealing, if possible, its full depth. The stage lights slowly dim to black, freaked by occasional drifts of smoke. Electronic music shimmers ominously. A glimmer at first, Sandy's chair and its occupant slowly materialize in mid-air between the proscenium and centre stage. A hologram. Sandy is writing. The hologram brightens and as suddenly fades, as the audience becomes aware of an identical figure in suspension high above their heads, held in a spotlight.

DEAR BERYL,

Just a short note to say I've left home for an indefinite period of time. Between you and me, after you moved up to Surfer's Paradise and that little ethnic couple shifted in with their kiddie, there was only one word to describe Kia Ora, 36 Gallipoli Crescent: *purgatory*. Sheer purgatory. I can't say it wasn't a bit of a wrench at first when I decided to flit the nest, but those blessed Greeks carried on as though they owned the place. In point of established fact, come to think of it, they *did* own the place. I felt like an unwelcome guest in my own home, and the last straw came when they chucked out my smoker's companion and paved the lawn.

Before I packed it in, for some strange reason I had a bit of a wander from room to room, though it would have broken your heart to see some of the colour schemes and general decor the Cosmopolis couple have introduced. Do you remember the number of *Home Beautiful*s we perused together before the war just to get the bathroom tiles right? I liked the beige mottled ones but you were dead set on the pale green. In the end we worked out a friendly compromise: mottled eau-de-nil with a little thin silver liner tile runing round below the dado.

Do you remember after the Depression, when Gallipoli Crescent was just paddocks and there was nothing between here and that red brick corner shop with the Velvet Soap advertisement all over the side wall? It was a newsagent's and a lolly shop before the war, with a penny Nestlé's machine[1] outside, then it was a ham and beef shop, then Moran & Cato's grocery[2] before the Nyal chemist shop went up next door. That turned into a knitting shop as I recall until they bowled down the verandah and made it an espresso bar. Well, they pulled down the Chinese takeaway last week and lo and behold! up there on the exposed wall was that old blue and silver Velvet ad, like it had only been painted yesterday.

Remember how we used to go to Glen Iris on a Sunday afternoon just to look at our block of land? When the builder started, we'd sit on the joists with a Thermos and a pile of *Home Beautiful*s while Kia Ora took shape week by week. Remember the Angelo brothers, Terrazzo Specialists, who'd come all the way over from Northcote to do the front porch and the bathroom floor without the faintest idea that in a few years' time they'd be bunged into an internment camp for the duration?

Remember all those little chips of marble, all

---

1 • A machine dispensing, for a penny, little, thin, wrapped slivers of chocolate.

2• A long-estalbished firm of family grocers, now defunct.

▬▬▬

shapes and sizes, on the bathroom floor? I used to study them every morning, sitting on the Armitage, trying to take my mind off the fact that nothing was happening. There was one like a shoe and another like a map of New Zealand and another looking a bit like a Scottie dog upside down. Remember Scottie dogs, Beryl? They were all the rage at one stage of the game and I gave you one for Mother's Day to take your mind off what the Specialist said. Boy, did we have fun thinking up an unusual name for that little feller. But we didn't have Scottie long as it eventuated. In point of fact, only about as long as it takes a lively little black Scotch terrier to toddle halfway across the street in front of a brand new Oldsmobile sedan. Remember how we felt sorry for the driver, standing there on the porch with Scottie wrapped up in that night's *Herald* holding out a bent Tailwagger's Club badge and saying, 'I'm sorry. I'm terribly sorry. I'm sorry about this. I'm sorry.'

Remember I told you I'd go down to the Louisa Hutchinson Lost Dog Kennels and get a replacement but you didn't enthuse and you never wore your Scottie dog brooch after that? It's funny, isn't it, how you never see Scottie dogs any more? They used to be everywhere but now they've disappeared. Whatever happened to the Scotch Terrier community? Perhaps they probably all got run over.

Remember how your mother used to say it was too far out, Glen Iris? And it was, before the war, although Ian Preston built in Oakleigh and his place stood out like a sore thumb for years with nothing but paddocks between them and Warrigal Road. Nothing but paddocks until the fifties when the cream brick veneers with the big chubby feature chimneys shot up like mushies making the Prestons' old rough-cast Californian bungalow, with its leadlight windows, look like a poor little grey relation. Remember that red flowering gum we used to see on the nature strip on top of the hill when we drove back home after a spin to Mordialloc, or Aspendale, or even Seaford, on a Sunday afternoon? Gone now since they widened the road. So much gone now you stop missing things.

Went into town the other day for a bit of a potter around. Always liked that trip on the number 6 tram, strap-hanging and reading the adverts.

Always was plenty to read on long tram rides too. Artgraf Photographic Studios, Peter Fox, Pelaco Shirts – 'Mine Tinkit They Fit', Copolov's Carpets, Guest's Famous Biscuits, Black and White Cigarettes, Berkowitz Lounge Suites, Stamina Cloth, Fantales, The Bambi Smith School of Charm, Did you Protex yourself this morning? *Someone isn't using Amplex ...*

Remember how we used to enjoy a trip into the city? We'd pop into Foy & Gibson's for a pair of Gibsonia blankets. Then you'd always like a bit of a browse around Manton's and Hicks Atkinson while I nipped across to the Leviathan or Buckley & Nunn's for a nice new suit or a serviceable sports coat. We'd meet up for a spot of lunch at Russell Collins or the Wild Cherry or even a crumbed fillet of whiting at the Wattle with poppies on the table and kisses on the cakestand, before we toddled down to Elizabeth Street where you always liked to pick up a new Georgette Heyer at Robinson and Mullens. On the odd shopping expedition when you wanted a bit of time on your ownsome to browse around the Myer Emporium, Paynes Bon Marché and the Mutual – 'there's a Mutual Store right near *your* door' – I was perfectly happy to slip into the

Times Theatrette or the Albany for an informative newsreel, and very occasionally I might have even enjoyed a Pony at Richardson's or the Cathedral or Phair's or Hosie's or the Wool Exchange, depending on what particular part of town I happened to be in.

Remember when we joined the Smileaway Club and used to nip into the 3DB 3LK auditorium on Saturday mornings for a spot of community singing with Dick Cranbourne and Mabel Nelson at the piano? Some of the ladies used to bring a bag of peas and a colander so they could shell them while they sang:

> If a grey haired lady says,
> How's your father?;
> that will be Mademoiselle ...
> Run rabbit, run rabbit, Hey
> little hen, when when
> when you grow too old to
> Dream when you're feeling blue birds
> over, the white ...
> Christmas.

Lovely old songs they were too. These days they call them 'nostalgic', although I can't recall anyone calling them that at the time.

Remember Tiny Snell's Community Hymn

Singing from the Prahran Town Hall on 3UZ? We always used to listen to those hymns ... religiously.

There used to be a lot of community singing on the wireless when we were young, plus Hawaiian music and yodelling. We tuned in religiously to *Dick Fair's Amateur Hour* too, and there was always at least one yodeller and someone having a crack at a few sacred numbers too, like 'Bless This House', the Lord's Prayer and the 'Green Eyed Dragon'. Dick Fair was always exceptionally, well ... fair, even when one of the particular artists forgot the words in the middle of 'Begin the Beguine' and had to begin the beguine about three times before he could finish it. Where it ended.

Remember how you always wanted me to go on the Amateur Hour or be one of the artists on Christie's Radio Auditions with John McMahon singing 'The Open Road' or 'Trees', but I said I would rather fly to the moon than make a silly galoot of myself on the wireless?

> Underneath the table on the kitchen floor
> Dressed in daddy's dressing-gown

There's a little fellow we adore

A little king without a crown ...

Funnily enough, that melody was on the hit parade when we were trying for a family although once at the tennis club when I said we were trying for a family you gave me a hard time later for being a bit on the crudish side. You reckoned it was OK to want a family or to *have* a family, but it was very uncalled for to *try* for one in mixed company. In point of actual fact, that was about the time we stopped trying, funnily enough.

You don't hear community singing these days — no Sir-ee![3] I'm blowed if I know what's become of the community singing community. It's hard to imagine a lot of young people in this day and age rushing into town so they could all shell peas and sing 'Wish Me Luck As You Wave Me Goodbye' over the air for nothing.

These days people won't even get off their backsides unless there's a chance of winning two Holden Geminis or a luxury all-expenses-paid trip for two to Surfer's or Manila.

Mind you, kiddies these days wouldn't know the old songs; don't even ask the Elderly Community to sing them either, not like we used to. I

---

3 • A catch-phrase of the early 1940s, also the refrain of a popular song, 'Franklin D. Roosevelt Jones', now rarely whistled.

remember, I always used to get my father to sing some of the old hits:

> Stop the cab, stop the cab
> Hey, heave wo!
> Somebody hold the horse's head and don't
> leave go
> But nevertheless, they had to confess
> Although they made a grab
> They never discovered the mystery of the
> hansom cab.[4]

Always used to be a few hansoms at the top of Bourke Street near the Eastern Market but you wouldn't recognize that part of town now, no more than you'd know the Paris End of Collins Street. More like the Sydney end of Collins Street these days. Or even the Bourke Street end of Collins Street.

The world's getting smaller. And taller. In my day you could see the You Yangs[5] from the top of the Manchester Unity.[6] In point of fact, there were umpteen places in town you could see the You Yangs from, whereas today with all the con-

---

4 • *Mystery of the Hansom Cab.* A reference to the musical stage version of the best-selling Melbourne-based thriller of 1888, written by the prolific New Zealand romancer Fergus Hume (1859–1932).

5 • Aboriginal for hill. A minor range of hills to the north-west of Melbourne, often the subject of Fred Williams, the popular author of boardroom landscapes.

6 • A seminal Melbourne skyscraper with imposing ziggurat.

struction and urban refurbishment you can hardly see past the next unfinished glass highrise and all you see is yourself in them. No one seems to be interested in seeing the You Yangs from anywhere any more, even if they were standing on Arthur's Seat staring the You Yangs in the face. I wonder if they're still there? Come to think about it, the only people with any time for the You Yangs at all these days is the Japanese tourist community and they've probably bought them. We never actually visited the You Yangs but we both had a lot of time for the Grampians. Remember our honeymoon, not long after the Depression, up at the old Bellfield Hotel? It was the height of luxury in those days, although the amenities were a considerable distance down the passage. It was pretty nippy in the mornings too, and I'll never forget hopping out of bed for a trip up the passage, and feeling my feet hit the cold lino ... and the smell of curried sausages: funnily enough, they don't seem to serve those lovely big brekkies any more in this day and age for some strange reason.

Well, Beryl, that's about it for the moment. I hope you are having an enjoyable time up at the Gold Coast and the mosquitos aren't giving you too much strife. Remember those Christmas holidays down at Bonbeach and Frankston and Sorrento before the war? Boy, you certainly got through the Citronella.[7] The mozzies used to love you, for some strange reason. Well, Beryl, I'd better sign off now. When you get this out of the blue you will more than likely think you're dreaming — and you will be. We all will be.

> Your ever loving,
> Sandy.

• *The suspended Sandy vanishes. On stage, slowly, by some system of photographic projection, and resembling the visions of Utamaro or the Euganean Hills[8] as they may sometimes be discerned from Venice on a pellucid October afternoon, appears the spectre of the You Yangs.*

---

7 • A dependable repellent.

8 • 'Those famous Euganean hills
     which bear,
   As seen from Lido through the
      harbour piles,
   The likeness of a clump of peakèd
      isles'

                    (*Shelley*)

Appendix A

—

THE POLKINGHORN LETTERS

—

THE SO-CALLED 'POLKINGHORN LETTERS' (also known as the 'Dear Graham' letters), written on sugar-pink stationery, were a favourite party piece of mine in the mid-fifties. The recital of this mindless, mind-numbing trivia, designed to bore the audience into submission or revolt, was later refined to a high art by Sandy himself. (See 'Dear Beryl', page 10 and 'The Land of the Living', page 71.)

• 1 •

36 Stoddart St,
Glen Iris.

2nd March

GRAHAM DARLING,

I do hope you are looking after yourself. Is your cold better yet. Those English winters must be dreadful. Are you wearing the cardigan I sent you. You haven't told me how you liked the colour, I chose your favourite darling.

Things are much the same here and all the neighbours ask after you. Mrs Kendall asks to be remembered. I have kept your room just as you left it. Not too tidy as I know how you used to hate your mother fussing all the time and cleaning up so that you could never find things when you wanted them.

I don't think I told you about last Sunday in my last letter. I had a lovely day. Mr and Mrs Clarke took me for a drive up to Ferntree Gully in the Hillman. We left early and stopped at a very nice place for lunch. I had a lovely salad. It was all very clean and nice. Then we drove into the mountains

▬▬▬

a little and parked the car. The view was a picture, I wish you could have been there dear.

We got home before dark and I asked the Clarkes in for a bite of tea but they were expecting their sister and her husband over for 500 so they couldnt stay. He is a very careful driver so you neednt have worried darling. They both asked to be remembered to you.

Well dear, I hope you can read this pencil as I can't find the pen. Look after yourself and write soon.

> Your Ever Loving
>> Mother. XXXXXXXXXXX

• 2 •

> 36 Stoddart St,
>> Glen Iris.

> 5th March

GRAHAM DARLING,

How is your cold. It seems ages since I heard from you but I suppose the mail from England gets delayed. Are you looking after yourself. Don't forget to wear the cardigan I sent you. Did you notice it was green – your favourite colour.

I saw old Mrs Kendall the other day and she said to be remembered to you. Everything is just the same at home and I have kept your room just as you left it dear. I keep the blind down in the afternoon so as not to fade your rug. Autumn is on the way and the Autumn light fades things so they say.

Did I tell you what a lovely time I had the other Sunday. The Clarkes took me for a lovely drive up to Ferntree Gully. It was a lovely day and Mr Clarke is a very careful driver so you needn't worry. We stopped at a nice clean place called the 'Dew-Drop Inn' and I had a lovely salad. It was all very fresh and clean. Then we drove into the mountains for a bit and parked the car at the lookout. You should have been there darling. The view was a picture.

We got back to Stoddart St by five so as not to make it a long day, and I asked the Clarkes in for a bit of tea. However Mrs Clarke was expecting her sister and husband over for 500 so they couldnt stay. Both asked to be remembered to you darling.

■■■■

Must close now as it is nearly time for my session. Look after yourself and write soon.

Your Ever Loving

Mother. XXXXXXXXXX

• 3 •

36 Stoddart St,

Glen Iris.

7th March

MY DARLING GRAHAM,

Just a short note to keep you up to date with the news. I hope you are looking after yourself. Those English winters must be dreadful. Autumn is on the way here and I pull down your blind every afternoon to keep the sun off your rug.

They say the Autumn light fades things. You will be pleased to hear that I have been getting about lately. You know how I hate being in a rut.

Mr and Mrs Clarke very kindly took me for a drive the other day. Mister Clarke is a very careful driver and it was a perfect day. We went to

Ferntree Gully and stopped at a lovely place for lunch. It was nice and clean and I had a beautiful salad. I can't remember the name of the place but I think I have written it down somewhere. We must both go there for a meal when you come home. Anyway, after that we drove into the mountains for a bit and Mr Clarke stopped the car at the lookout. The view was an absolute picture. I couldn't help wishing you were there, darling.

To cut a long story short we got home before tea and I asked the Clarkes to pop in for a bite of tea. But Mrs Clarke was expecting her sister and her husband over for solo so they couldn't spare the time. Anyway there's always another time I said.

Look after yourself dear and don't forget to wear the green cardi I sent you. How is your cold?

Mr and Mrs Clarke and Mrs Kendall ask to be remembered to you.

Your Ever Loving

Mother. XXXXXXXXXXXX

• 4 •

36 Stoddart St,

Glen Iris.

13th March

MY DEAREST GRAHAM,

Just a short note this time as it is nearly time for my session. How is that cold of yours. The English winters must be dreadful. Look after yourself darling and keep yourself wrapped up. I sent you a lovely green cardigan which I hope you are wearing. Look after yourself now.

Mrs Kendall spoke to me the other day and asks to be remembered to you. So do Mr and Mrs Clarke.

What a kind couple they are! On Sunday they took me for a lovely drive to Ferntree Gully in the Hillman. We stopped for lunch at a very clean little place and I had a really beautiful salad. It was all so fresh and clean. Afterwards we drove further on to the lookout and everything was a picture.

He is such a careful driver and dropped me off at the front door. They couldn't come in for tea because they were expecting her sister and husband over. Still, there's always a next time.

I think that's about all the news at the moment. Things are just the same at home darling and I have just pulled down the blind in your room.

Mrs Kendall asked to be remembered to you. Don't forget to look after yourself and write again soon.

Your Ever Loving

Mother. XXXXXXXXXXX

• 5 •

36 Stoddart St,
Glen Iris.

20th March.

MY OWN DARLING GRAHAM,

I haven't got much new for you this time. Things at home are just about the same and I have kept your room exactly as you left it dear.

The Clarkes gave me a beautiful time yesterday.

He is a very careful driver and we went for a short trip to Ferntree Gully. On the way we had lunch as a very clean place where I had a beautiful salad. It was really lovely. After that we drove on into the mountains and Mr Clarke stopped the car at the lookout. I wish you had been there. Mrs Clarke was expecting people over so they couldn't stay but perhaps another time she said. The view was a real picture. I wish you could have been there.

Look after yourself dear and don't forget to wrap yourself up. Those English winters must be dreadful. Must close now as I must pull down your blind before my session comes on. The Autumn sun fades things. Look after yourself and don't forget to wear your cardi.

Your Ever Loving

Mother. XXXXXXXX

· 6 ·

8 Stoddart St,

Glen Iris.

1st April.

DEAR GRAHAM,

Geoff and I wish to convey our deepest sympathy on the occasion of your mother's sudden passing last week. It was a terrible shock to us all as she had always been in such good health.

We had not seen her since a short drive to Ferntree Gully about a month ago when she seemed in the best of spirits. We left at morning tea time and stopped for lunch on the road at quite a nice little place we know of. She appeared to thor-oughly enjoy her salad and the rest of the trip generally.

Geoff is a very careful driver and we drove up to the lookout to show your mother the view.

We got her home by six and she was very anxious that we should stay to tea. The poor soul looked very tired and we had to go to church anyway so we promised to come next time.

That was the last time I saw her. Mrs Kendall was at the funeral and asks to be remembered to you. She sends her condolences.

Our deepest sympathy in your bereavement.

Yours sincerely,

Edna Clarke.

Appendix B

SANDY STONE'S BIG WEEK

By H. GRAHAME

SANDY STONE appeared in public for the first time in the following story, published in a 1958 issue of the long-defunct Canberra student magazine *Prometheus*. The pseudonymous 'H. Grahame' is, of course, Barry Humphries.

SANDY STONE lived in a very nice home in Hartwell. On summer evenings after tea he was frequently to be found moving about his front lawn with a hose, soaking the warm shrubs and darkening the light-coloured soil with water. For this job Sandy wore a white open-necked shirt and an old pair of khaki shorts.

It was very restful moving about like that in the half light playing the loud jet of water on his shrubs.

Over the low fences on either side, or across the street, Sandy often saw neighbours engaged in similar restful tasks. Mr Whittle, who was always very late home from work, passed at this hour, and the two men said 'night to each other across the front fence.

Towards half-past seven the crickets became very shrill, whistling like a host of tireless postmen, and darkness slowly descended on the rows of neat gardens in Humoureske Street. Soon, all that was visible of Sandy Stone was his white bulky shirt and the white arc of water from his hose.

He heard the voice of his wife calling; breaking into his thoughts and then becoming part of them. Soon he had stopped the throbbing tap, disconnected the hose, and put it, neatly coiled, in the tool shed.

The kitchen was bright and yellow after the dark of the garden, and he stood therefore for a moment inhaling the odour of freshly baked sponge fingers. Beryl was busy getting things ready for the Stubbings, who were coming over for five hundred tomorrow night. She loved to get things like that over and done with and out of the way.

Sandy went through into the lounge room and turned on the wireless. It was still early, but they hated missing *You've Got to be in It*. Mantovani's 'Victor Herbert Suite' filled the room and Sandy settled himself heavily in the burgundy crushed velvet armchair and rolled a cigarette. For a big stocky man his fingers seemed oddly girlish as they fashioned the little cylinder. But then, he had really been fairly slight before he was married. Twenty-eight years of Beryl's good home cooking had wrought the change. Now he had what other people's children called 'a real pot'; it strained inside the tight khaki shorts as he stretched out in the armchair smoking. Sometimes he blew the smoke straight at an unblinking kookaburra, hand-painted on the lampshade.

Sandy's small grey eyes, for no reason, looked round the room. Opposite his chair were the double doors into the dining room, and through those two panels of rippled glass decorated with orange chevrons and other motifs of the thirties he could see the yellow entrance to the kitchen beyond. The light from the lamp above the console wireless fell across Sandy's lap and caught a hint of gold in the sparse down above his red knees. It glinted too on the books beside the fireplace; on the spine of *The Family Doctor* and the heavily gilt *Story of the World in Pictures*. Somehow, too, the lamplight hit the glass of their wedding photo on the mantelpiece, effacing all detail. Just turning it into a vacant pane of glass.

Sandy breathed the caramel odour of cooking and thought of the Stubbings coming over for five hundred tomorrow night. They'd better not stay too late, he thought, as Friday was always busy at work and he would want to feel fresh for Friday night when he always went to the RSL at Gallipoli Hall. He was local treasurer and couldn't miss out very well. It was quite a week when he came to think about it. On Saturday night they had tickets for the tennis picture night at the Rivoli. Should be a good show too: Bob Hope. A laugh's as good as a tonic these days, he thought. Then, the special memorial service at Holy Trinity on Sunday night. A big week!

'Arthur, before I forget!' said Beryl, who had come in to turn up the wireless.

'And pull the smoker's stand over next to the chair instead of reaching out and putting ash on my carpet. I only did it this morning.' She dried her hands on a pretty apron.

'I can't get down to the junction tomorrow, so would you buy some cashews on your way home? The Stubbings like them.'

An unreal voice bellowed: 'You've got to be in it – *to win it*!'

Sandy said he would.

Appendix C

———

ANZAC SANDY

———

THAT I HAD TOYED with the idea of making Sandy a Gallipoli veteran is revealed in a fragment never performed which I wrote in 1968 in the form of another letter to Beryl.

Hilton Hotel
Istanbul

25th April, 1968

DEAR BERYL,

We have just got back to the hotel after a very tiring day sight-seeing so as you can imagine I feel

———

a bit of a cot-case. The Qantas chappie has been particularly helpful, nothing has been too much trouble and the trip out to Gallipoli this morning was a real experience. There weren't many of us but they turned on a Turkish guide who spoke perfect Australian and he seemed a very nice type of chappie. He put over a nice little speech about Anzac Day and how there was a fair bit to be said for both sides as far as bravery and that was concerned. To tell you the truth he seemed to know more about the whole blooming issue than we did who actually were there at the time of hostilities, which amused me because at the time (1915 that is) he couldn't have been more than a hop floating around in his old man's beer. Be that as it may, a few of the different ones got a snap of him with Gallipoli in the background and at the end of the tour we all chipped in a few bob just to show there were no hard feelings.

I got quite a bit of footage with my little Jap job so with a bit of luck you'll see it all for yourself on the lounge-room wall when I get back to Melbourne. It's still all a bit like a dream thinking of all those years ago with your cobbers being blown to smithereens and the snow and mud and that. I remember how we used to sit in the dugouts yarning away about tucker and tobacco and home and that.

The old place doesn't look that different as far as I can remember and it hasn't changed as much as we have. And some of the graves have been kept up something beautiful. Anyway it was a real scorcher of a day and most of us had to go pretty easy though naturally there was the odd one or two who had to go climbing round on the cliffs to get the odd souvenir snap. There was one chappie called Steve Arblaster who I was chinwagging to only the other day in the plane. He was a New Zealander but quite a nice type of chappie. Anyway it turned out he was a bit of a ratbag because this morning he insisted on climbing up one of the cliffs to get a coloured slide of the beach though we all reckoned he was dippy to try because he could easily come a cropper on his neck. Sure enough the next thing I heard was that he'd fallen all right and done his hip. The poor old beggar had asked for it but I couldn't help thinking that Gallipoli is still bloody dangerous, even fifty-three years later.

Anyway that just about put the kibosh on the whole trip, so we called it a day. This hotel is called the Istanbul Hilton and it's just about as modern as tomorrow though I'm going easy on the Turkish tucker just in case I run into the odd bit of tummy trouble and seeing as we won the war in the end I wouldn't want to push me luck.

Anyway, Beryl, I just had a yarn about the old times over a jar or two with some of the boys and the general consensus of opinion was that the trip was well worth while. I always wanted to nip back and take another decko at Anzac Cove and Lemnos and Samothrace and some of the other historical Australian places in peace time. It took me a good while to get around to it I know but it was all still there – the beach, gum tree flat, Hill 60, Bottom's Ridge, the whole blessed issue. Look after yourself now,

Your ever loving,

Sandy

Wally Saunders, Alf Crocker and old Percy Griffiths would like to be remembered.

FOR THE BEST IN PAPERBACKS, LOOK FOR THE 🐧

In every corner of the world, on every subject under the sun, Penguin represents quality and variety – the very best in publishing today.

For complete information about books available from Penguin – including Puffins, Penguin Classics and Arkana – and how to order them, write to us at the appropriate address below. Please note that for copyright reasons the selection of books varies from country to country.

In the United Kingdom: Please write to *Dept E.P., Penguin Books Ltd, Harmondsworth, Middlesex, UB7 0DA*.

If you have any difficulty in obtaining a title, please send your order with the correct money, plus ten per cent for postage and packaging, to *PO Box No 11, West Drayton, Middlesex*

In the United States: Please write to *Dept BA, Penguin, 299 Murray Hill Parkway, East Rutherford, New Jersey 07073*

In Canada: Please write to *Penguin Books Canada Ltd, 2801 John Street, Markham, Ontario L3R 1B4*

In Australia: Please write to the *Marketing Department, Penguin Books Australia Ltd, P.O. Box 257, Ringwood, Victoria 3134*

In New Zealand: Please write to the *Marketing Department, Penguin Books (NZ) Ltd, Private Bag, Takapuna, Auckland 9*

In India: Please write to *Penguin Overseas Ltd, 706 Eros Apartments, 56 Nehru Place, New Delhi, 110019*

In the Netherlands: Please write to *Penguin Books Netherlands B.V., Postbus 195, NL–1380AD Weesp*

In West Germany: Please write to *Penguin Books Ltd, Friedrichstrasse 10–12, D–6000 Frankfurt/Main 1*

In Spain: Please write to *Alhambra Longman S.A., Fernandez de la Hoz 9, E–28010 Madrid*

In Italy: Please write to *Penguin Italia s.r.l., Via Como 4, I-20096 Pioltello (Milano)*

In France: Please write to *Penguin Books Ltd, 39 Rue de Montmorency, F-75003 Paris*

In Japan: Please write to *Longman Penguin Japan Co Ltd, Yamaguchi Building, 2–12–9 Kanda Jimbocho, Chiyoda-Ku, Tokyo 101*

A CHOICE OF PENGUIN FICTION

A Natural Curiosity Margaret Drabble

Moving effortlessly from black comedy to acute social observation, Margaret Drabble picks up the thread of the characters and stories of *The Radiant Way*, as her engrossing panorama of the way we are today shifts to the north of England. 'Confident and marvellously accomplished' – *London Review of Books*

Summer's Lease John Mortimer

'It's high summer, high comedy too, when Molly drags her amiably bickering family to a rented Tuscan villa for the hols ... With a cosy fluency of wit, Mortimer charms us into his urbane tangle of clues...' – *Mail on Sunday*. 'Superb' – Ruth Rendell

Nice Work David Lodge

'The campus novel meets the industrial novel ... compulsive reading' – David Profumo in the *Daily Telegraph*. 'A work of immense intelligence, informative, disturbing and diverting ... one of the best novelists of his generation' – Anthony Burgess in the *Observer*

S. John Updike

'John Updike's very funny satire not only pierces the occluded hocus-pocus of Lego religion which exploits the gullible and self-deluded ... but probes more deeply and seriously the inadequacies on which superstitious skulduggery battens' – *The Times*

The Counterlife Philip Roth

'Roth has now surpassed himself' – *Washington Post*. 'A breathtaking *tour de force* of wit, wisdom, ingenuity and sharply-honed malice' – *The Times*